23. Edwin Booth as Iago in William Shakespeare's *Othello* by Thomas Hicks.

PORTRAITS OF THE AMERICAN STAGE
1771-1971

An Exhibition in Celebration of the Inaugural Season
of The John F. Kennedy Center for the Performing Arts

Published for

THE NATIONAL PORTRAIT GALLERY

by the Smithsonian Institution Press

City of Washington · 1971

Library of Congress Card Number 75-170284.

For sale by the Superintendent of Documents, U.S. Government Printing Office, Washington, D.C. 20402 · Stock number 4700-0181 · Price $4.50

Photographs by the lending institutions or the National Portrait Gallery except catalog numbers: 66, 73, 74, Brenwasser; 5, 15, 25, 26, 44, 46, 65, 72, 83, Geoffrey Clements; 16, Edward Connacchio; 78, P. Richard Eells; 2, Jim Hayman; 88, Peter A. Juley & Son; 56, 85, John D. Schiff; 31, 69, 70, Joseph Szaszfai; 22, Roy Trahan.

COVER ILLUSTRATIONS: *94. Tragedy; 95. Comedy, by William Rush.*

Dimensions are given in inches, height preceding width.

Contents

American Ballet Theatre

American Shakespeare Festival Theatre

Anonymous Lenders

Leonard Bernstein

Arbit Blatas

Boston Museum of Fine Arts

Brown University

Buffalo Fine Arts Academy, Albright-Knox Gallery

University of California at Los Angeles, Dance Department

Boris Chaliapin

Mrs. Otis Chatfield-Taylor

Cincinnati Art Museum

Sterling and Francine Clark Art Institute

Colonial Williamsburg Foundation

Corcoran Gallery of Art

Charles Van Brunt Cushman

Dallas Civic Opera

Detroit Public Library

Eaves Costume Company

Mrs. Parmenia Migel Ekstrom

Miss Angna Enters

Furman Finck

Folger Shakespeare Library

John Foote

Edwin Forrest Home

Free Library of Philadelphia

Garrick Club, London

Benny Goodman

Mrs. Una Hanbury

Harvard Theatre Collection

Henry Harvitt

Haydn Museum, Eisenstadt, Austria

Al Hirschfeld

Hirschl and Adler Galleries

Historical Society of York County, York, Pennsylvania

Honolulu Academy of Arts

Mrs. Vladimir Horowitz

Indianapolis Museum of Art

Anne Jackson—Eli Wallach Collection

Kathryn Productions

Lawrence V. Kelly

Mrs. Jean Kling Lewton

Library of Congress

Alfred Lunt

Lyric Opera of Chicago

Count Cyril McCormack

Lauritz Melchior

Metropolitan Museum of Art

Metropolitan Opera Association

Metropolitan Opera Guild

Milwaukee Art Center

National Gallery of Art

National Portrait Gallery, London

New Orleans Public Library

New York Public Library at Lincoln Center

New-York Historical Society

New York State Historical Association

Museum of the City of New York

Donald Oenslager

Peabody Institute

Pennsylvania Academy of the Fine Arts

Mrs. Edward Pflueger

Phillips Collection

Playboy

The Players

Portsmouth Little Theatre, Portsmouth, Ohio

Miss Leontyne Price

Francis Robinson

Arthur Rubinstein

Peter A. Salm

Ted Shawn

Mrs. Rosemarie Sloat

Steinway and Sons

Stephens College

Miss Dorothy Stickney

Miss Barbra Streisand

Theatre Guild Archives

Time

Robert L. B. Tobin

United States Marine Corps Museum

Victoria and Albert Museum

Wadsworth Atheneum

Mrs. Leonard Warren

Whitney Museum of American Art

Worcester Art Museum

Yale University Library

Marvin Sadik
Director

It is a genuine pleasure for the National Portrait Gallery to present these "Portraits of the American Stage" at the opening of the inaugural season of The John F. Kennedy Center for the Performing Arts. A gallery is a kind of theater, and exhibitions are in a special way stage productions. But rarely are they as close in subject to the real thing as is this exhibition. The illustrious company whose portraits have been assembled here have, during the past two centuries, contributed unforgettable images to the American stage and have played a major role in the cultural life of the nation.

Many, if not all, of the early performers represented here were legends in their own day—Charlotte Cushman, Fanny Elssler, Jenny Lind, Edwin Booth, and Joseph Jefferson, to invoke the names of only a handful of superstars. Also included from these years are figures such as Ira Aldridge and Augusta Maywood, who, though born in this country, won their greatest fame abroad. Aldridge first played Othello in 1825 at the Theatre Royal in Brighton and was later hailed by London critics as "a star of the first magnitude"; Maywood became prima ballerina at Vienna's Hofbergoperntheater in 1845 and later shared this title with Fanny Elssler at La Scala in Milan.

Equally famous as artists during this period are the painters of some of the portraits on view—Charles Willson Peale, John Neagle, Thomas Sully, Henry Inman, Eastman Johnson, and John Singer Sargent. To this list of renowned Americans must be added two great Frenchmen: Toulouse-Lautrec, creator of the stunning lithograph of the incandescent Loie Fuller, born in Fullersburg, Illinois; and Auguste Rodin, sculptor of the small bronze of the immortal Duse, whose last performance was in Pittsburgh, Pennsylvania.

It has seemed to me that the art of portraiture has a special quality in connection with the stage, for the stage is an ephemeral artistic medium. The playwright leaves a play, the composer a score, the performer—a performance. Iago lives, but Edwin Booth dies. The great performance comes down to us as echo and reecho of criticism and applause, the performer as a memory. The portrait of a consummate artist of the dramatic, operatic, or concert stage, seized from life, tends to be more than a mere record of appearance, more than a characterization of personality—it can evoke the veritable quintessence of a presence and a performance otherwise lost.

How doubly fortunate, then, are the visitors to this exhibition and the readers of this catalog for whom these likenesses of such immortals as Loie Fuller, Eleonora Duse, Sarah Bernhardt, Maude Adams, Nijinsky, and Paderewski will recall a living performance!

Special thanks must be given to those whose generous assistance and cooperation have given this exhibition and this catalog whatever merit they possess. His Excellency Dr. Karl Gruber, Ambassador of Austria, and Dr. Peter Niesner, his Cultural Attaché, willingly aided in the negotiations to bring the portrait of Fanny Elssler from the Haydn Museum. The early interest of Staats Cotsworth and the late Dennis King made possible the borrowing of works from the extraordinary art collection of The Players. Miss Genevieve Oswald and Miss Marta Lucyshyn of the Dance Collection, Library of the Performing Arts, New York, have been mentors and advisers in matters concerning the dance. Miss Helen Willard of the Harvard Theatre Collection and Sam Pearce of the Museum of the City of New York have both been enthusiastic and generous. In London, Richard Ormond of the National Portrait Gallery and Oliver Davies of the Royal College of Music have been of invaluable assistance in the researching of English portraiture. At Washington's own Library of Congress, both Anthony Doherty and Milton Kaplan have never failed to respond graciously to my requests for information and aid. Mrs. Austin Lowrey III was most discriminating and helpful in searching the voluminous newspaper clipping files at the Library of the Performing Arts. Mrs. Parmenia Migel Ekstrom unselfishly made available to me, prior to their publication, her discoveries regarding the last days of Augusta Maywood. The entire staff of the National Portrait Gallery has been most understanding and cooperative, especially Mrs. Doris Rauch and Miss Suzanne Jenkins, who have tolerated an erratic taskmaster, typed his reams of letters and catalog notes, and corrected his lamentable spelling whenever necessary. Charles J. E. Kelly has been a merciless, but valuable, critic of my ideas for this exhibition, and the memory of Mrs. Naomi Vincent Butler, sometime actress, colleague and friend, has been a constant inspiration.

Acknowledgments

Monroe H. Fabian
Associate Curator

English-speaking America saw an amateur production of a play as early as 1665—on the Eastern Shore of Virginia—and the first performance in a building constructed especially as a theater took place in Williamsburg in 1718. The first formally organized troupe of performers was established in Philadelphia in 1749 and was promptly run out of town by the Quaker-dominated City Council. The Quakers obviously did not share the urbane attitudes of the Church of England colonists farther south. Boston's puritan ethic was also unreceptive to people of the stage. New York, Annapolis, Williamsburg, and much to the chagrin of the Quakers, Southward, just over the city line from Philadelphia, became the principal theater towns in America.

Monroe H. Fabian
Associate Curator

Touring Companies had been traveling the eastern seaboard for at least twenty-five years, and conditions had begun to look hopeful for actors, singers, and instrumentalists when troubled times began in the 1770s. On 20 October 1774 the performing arts in all the colonies came to a halt when the Continental Congress, meeting in Philadelphia, passed a resolution condemning "shews, plays, and other expensive diversions and entertainments" for the duration of the war. Quakers and puritans must have been ecstatic. Except for a few dramatic presentations by British occupation troops, it was not until after the Revolution that plays, operas, dances, and concerts returned and became a major feature of American urban life.

Pictorial material from the first century of the performing arts in America is exceedingly rare. We can learn the names and something of the personalities of the early performers from the playbills, diary entries, and newspapers of the times, but their physical appearance in almost all cases is unknown to us. In collections on both sides of the Atlantic, only a small handful of prints and one painting of an eighteenth-century artist of the American stage survive. The one painting, appropriately enough, is of the lovely young actress Nancy Hallam, America's first matinee idol and a member of the American Company of Comedians, which was organized by the immigrant actor David Douglass, and was one of the most important theatrical companies in the colonial era. The portrait was painted in Annapolis and was exhibited there exactly two hundred years ago.

With this unique icon of the early days of the arts of entertainment in the United States in its proper place of precedence, the exhibition presents portraits of ninety-one noted actors, actresses, singers, dancers, instrumentalists, and conductors. It will be noted immediately that quite a few of these personalities were foreign born. Since their beginnings our theaters have been host to visitors from abroad, and since the early decades of the nineteenth century our native-born performers have appeared with acclaim outside our country. Consequently the smug chauvinism that would limit this exhibition to persons who were and are citizens of the United States has been resisted in order to better exhibit the international aspects of America's involvement in the performing arts. The artistry of a Jenny Lind, an Enrico Caruso, or an Anna Pavlova would not have been enhanced by American citizenship, nor would these performers' influence on our culture have been any more real for it.

The most noteworthy portrait of a performer available for this exhibition has been selected regardless of its place of origin, but a special effort has been made to obtain those which were created as a result of professional activity in this country. Costume pictures were chosen if they give the best impression of a performer's career. Portraits of a number of personalities not included in the exhibition would have been significant additions to these assembled here if they had been available. Unfortunately, many luminaries of the American stage have never been depicted by painter, sculptor, or graphic artist. Portraits of others have been lost, and portraits of still others could not be borrowed, these latter including Andy Warhol's multiple-image picture of the dancer Merce Cunningham and a particularly lovely costume picture of the legendary soprano Maria Malibran. The void left by portraits such as these is at least partially filled by the inclusion in the exhibition of the only known life portrait of Ira Aldridge, the first native American performer to win international renown, and the Henry Inman painting of the ballerina Fanny Elssler, which, although painted in New York, has no record of previous exhibition in this country. Self-portraits of stage personalities are exceedingly rare, but there are two in the exhibition, those of the dancer John Durang and comedian Zero Mostel.

This exhibition is limited to those personalities of the American stage whose primary achievements have been in the drama, dance, opera, musical comedy, and on the concert stage. Covering as it does two centuries of the American stage, the exhibition necessarily omits the great personalities of the film, television, and radio.

With the portraits are exhibited numerous costumes and items of manuscript and memorabilia, making tangible the careers of the performers featured in this exhibition. Nobody can deny the prominent place of the performing arts in the history of the United States. If an exhibition of its luminaries needs justification, let it come from that most revered of American actors, Edwin Booth. Writing in 1886, Mr. Booth noted:

In my study . . . I have often sat until dawn, alternately reading memoirs of the great actors of the past, and contemplating their portraits and death-masks which hang upon the walls; and somehow I seem to derive a more satisfactory idea of their capabilities from their counterfeit presentments than from the written records of their lives.

Catalog of the Exhibition

Nancy Hallam   Most of the actors and actresses who came to America before the Revolution exist now only as names in brittle newspapers and playbills and in dry scholarly volumes. Nancy Hallam is one of very few who emerges from these dusty accounts as a real person. Some evidence of her winsome personality and her professional achievements is preserved, but very little is known of her life offstage. There is no record of when and where she was born—presumably in England in the second quarter of the century. There is no account of her first appearance in America, but she may have appeared here as early as 1758 playing juvenile roles in the Company of Comedians managed by David Douglass who was her uncle by marriage. There is no record of her death, although it may well have occurred in Jamaica where she married the organist of the parish church at Kingston on 15 May 1775. There is ample record, however, to show that she was the first of many players on the American stage to attract a loyal and vociferous following. She can be identified as one of several singers in a concert in St. Philip's Church in Charleston in October of 1765, and there are kind words in that city's press for her performance in *Cinthia* on 4 March 1766. For her benefit performance one month later she acted in the first performance of William Whitehead's *School for Lovers* that was seen in the English colonies. Traveling with Douglass's company, which had been rechristened the American Company of Comedians, she played Annapolis in the autumn of 1770. It was in that city—at the time one of the most genteel centers of life and culture in America—that the most important evidence of her popularity was preserved for us. Her Imogen in Shakespeare's *Cymbeline* inspired one anonymous correspondent of the *Maryland Gazette* to effusive praise. Printed with his letter were verses extolling the loveliness and talent of the young actress. They proved later to have been written by the Reverend Mr. Jonathan Boucher, rector of St. Ann's parish. Urged on by this extraordinary show of clerical enthusiasm for things secular, Charles Willson Peale painted Nancy Hallam as Imogen in a scene from act 3, scene 6. He chose the moment when Imogen, disguised as the boy Fidele, emerges from a cave where he or she has been hiding. When Nancy Hallam returned to Annapolis in September and October of 1771 both the real and the counterfeit actress were available for the admiration of her discriminating public.

1. Nancy Hallam as Imogen in Shakespeare's *Cymbeline*
by Charles Willson Peale, 1771
Oil on canvas, 50 x 40¼
Lent by Colonial Williamsburg Foundation

John Durang
1768-1822

At various times in his career in the theater John Durang was a dancer, a singer, a mime, a tightrope walker, a puppeteer, a scene painter, a manager, and an actor. In respect to this diversity it must be admitted that he probably had no more varied experience than many other stage-struck young men and women who had been lured by the bright lights of the fledgling American theater. Born in York, Pennsylvania, 6 January 1768, Durang seems to have made his debut in Philadelphia in December of 1784 with Lewis Hallam's company at the Southwark Theatre. The great war was still an unpleasant memory that reflected against the largely English company, and so John Durang, the only native-born of the group, was singled out for applause. His favorite contribution to an evening's entertainment seems to have been dancing the Hornpipe. In August of 1785 the Hallam company opened in New York where Durang was billed as Scaramouche in a harlequinade, *The Touchstone, or Harlequin Traveler*. His Hornpipe remained, however, both his and his audiences' favorite. After a season in New York, Durang was back in Philadelphia giving puppet plays in his family's house. In 1788 Durang joined Hallam's Old American Company again for seven years of touring. Early in the 1790s he was overshadowed by the talents of European-trained dancers who began to appear on American stages. In 1794 Durang danced an Indian dance in the premiere of *Tammany*, one of the first American operas with a native subject. The critics are silent as to the merits of our hero's contribution. At his benefit performance on 11 June 1794, Durang performed for the first time on the slack wire and may also have been the choreographer of the pantomime *The Huntress, or Tammany's Frolics*, which enshrined this astounding performance. He was all the while still dancing the Hornpipe at the slightest provocation. In 1796 he was a secondary dancer with the ballet company of Jean-Baptiste Francisque which attached itself to the Old American Company. From October 1796 until December of 1799 Durang performed with John B. Rickett's Circus in Philadelphia and New York. The summer of 1800 he became coimpresario with John B. Rowson at the Southwark Theatre. From that time on until his retirement from the stage in 1819, he was a member of the stock company of Philadelphia's Chestnut Street Theatre during the winter seasons. In the summers between 1808 and 1816 he formed his own company and toured the rural areas of Pennsylvania and Maryland. He was the star of his Pennsylvania German dialect productions of Shakespeare's *Taming of the Shrew* and *Richard III*. He retired from the stage in 1819 and settled permanently in Philadelphia, where he died on 29 March 1822.

2. John Durang's autograph memoir, written before 1822.
The volume contains six self-portrait watercolors
8⅛ x 6½
Lent by Historical Society of York County, York, Pennsylvania

John Durang in Character of a Hornpipe.

Mr. J. Durang in Character of Harlequin. Animation Scene.

Mr. Jn. Durang in Character, of a Highland Fling. Ballett of Auld Robin gray.

Mr. Jn. Durang in character of a Pas Seul a Vestris.

John Durang in Character of the Dutch Fisherman

Mr. Jn. Durang in character...

William Burke Wood
1779-1861

The stage debut of Montreal-born William Burke Wood took place in Annapolis in 1798. It occurred with a touring company managed by Thomas Wignell, and in December of that year Wood appeared for the first time with them on their home stage in Philadelphia. His career in the City of Brotherly Love was to last forty-eight years and thus encompass the most important formative period of the infant American Theatre. In 1810 he became comanager of the Chestnut Street theatre with his fellow actor, William Warren, and this association was to continue until 1826 when for a brief while he served as manager of the rival Arch Street Theatre. Leaving managership behind, he continued to act with various companies until his farewell on the stage of Philadelphia's Walnut Street Theatre on 18 November 1846. Wood published in 1855 his *Personal Recollections of the Stage,* a treasury of information concerning dramatic history and practice in America in the first half of the last century. He quotes no glowing reviews of his own performances, except for a justifiably detailed description of the farewell tendered to him in 1846. As an afterthought he cites his prodigious record of characterizations—342 roles in 199 plays—each born, no doubt, more out of the ever-present necessity which lightly cloaked the actors on the adolescent American stage, than any manifestation of dramatic genius. William Dunlap, the most proficient chronicler of the early nineteenth-century stage in the United States, found Wood's greatest ability in what we today would call drawing-room comedy, and then added, "he succeeds admirably well in tragedy, too." William Burke Wood died in Philadelphia on 23 September 1861.

3. William Burke Wood as Charles de Moor in Joseph Holman's
adaptation of Friedrich Schiller's *The Robbers*
by Thomas Sully, 1811
Oil on canvas, 42½ x 30⅛
Lent by Corcoran Gallery of Art

George Frederick Cooke
1756-1811

George Frederick Cooke had an erratic career of thirty-four years on the English stage before his first appearance in New York on 21 November 1810. His debut role, Richard III, was one of his most successful, His English career had been checkered owing to his frequent bouts with the bottle, but when he was sober he was quite frequently a brilliant actor and found a special success in those roles which showed greed and hypocrisy. However, these roles may have reflected his own defects of character, he was the first British actor of such high professional stature to grace the American stage, and his New York debut was triumphant. Box-office receipts, a major measure of an actor's success, were again very high when he made his first Philadelphia appearances in the following March. His intemperance caught up with him, however; he died at New York on 26 September 1811 and was buried in the cemetery of St. Paul's Church. In Philadelphia, Thomas Sully's painting of him as Richard III was placed on the shrouded stage of the Chestnut Street Theatre during a special tribute by the company. William B. Wood, manager of the theater, spoke very kindly of his abilities and personality in his reminiscences published some forty years later. He vouched for the portrait as a true rendering of Cooke's costume and facial expression. Edmund Kean, during his visit to America in the second decade of the nineteenth century, had Cooke's body reburied in St. Paul's cemetery beneath a fitting monument. We are told that during the reinterment he took for himself one of George Frederick Cooke's bones which he proudly kept as a relic of a man he considered one of the greatest English actors. He kept it, that is, until Mrs. Kean threw it out.

4. George Frederick Cooke in the title role of Shakespeare's *Richard III*
by Thomas Sully, 1811
Oil on canvas, 94 x 60

Lent by Pennsylvania Academy of the Fine Arts

Abandoned by his mother shortly after his birth out of wedlock on 4 November 1787, Edmund Kean rose literally from the gutters of London to one of the most prominent positions in the history of his profession. He is said to have begun his stage career at age three impersonating Cupid, and whatever the facts of his early career on the stage might be, we do know that his first appearance as Shylock in *The Merchant of Venice* at Drury Lane on 26 January 1814 is an event unmatched in importance in the annals of the drama in England. So powerful were his characterizations of this and other roles he essayed that season that the management cleared an unprecedented 20,000 pounds in four months. Benjamin West, this country's first expatriate painter, is said to have avowed that Kean's facial expression in *Richard III* kept him awake all night. We take that comment to be one great artist's praise for another. The theater-going public was as fickle then as it is now, and waning interest in England was no doubt part of the reason he elected to undertake a tour of the United States in 1820. His first appearance here was as Richard III with the Park Theatre Company at New York's Anthony Street Theatre on 29 November. He was, of course, a success, even though the newspapers took prejudiced stands for and against him. He appeared to great applause in Philadelphia, and William B. Wood in his *Recollections* credits Kean with instituting the theater custom we now accept as the prerogative of all dramatic artists, worthy and unworthy both—the final bow at the end of the play. With little sympathy for the ceremony, Mr. Wood wrote, "The absurdity of dragging out before the curtain a deceased Hamlet, Macbeth, or Richard in an exhausted state, merely to take a bow . . . is one which we date from this time." Shortly after beginning a second engagement in Boston on 23 May 1821, Kean refused to play before a light audience. The local newspapers were indignant and the attitude echoed in New York and Philadelphia. Kean canceled the remainder of his scheduled tour and returned to England, justified, however, in considering his American tour an unqualified dramatic success. Back home he became the object of public scorn when named as codefendant in a notorious divorce case, and he left again for a tour of the United States. News of his English nocturnal adventures preceded him, and he was treated as a villain by the American press. His second New York debut on 14 November 1825, again as Richard III, was greeted with both hisses and cheers and the remainder of his thirteen-month tour was to be punctuated with the same declamations. He considered his election as a chief of the Huron tribe in Quebec the highlight of his American career. He had visiting cards printed with "Edmund Kean" on one side and his Indian name, "Alanie-nouidet," on the other. His last American appearance was in New York on 5 December 1826. Returning to England his career and his health declined steadily. On 12 March 1833 he collapsed on the stage at Drury Lane and died on May 15.

5. Edmund Kean in the title role of Shakespeare's *Richard III*
by John Neagle, 1826
Oil on canvas, 26 x 21½
Lent by The Players

Junius Brutus Booth
1796–1852

Junius Brutus Booth made his stage debut at an amateur theater in London in 1813. Within two years he had been engaged for a season at Covent Garden. On 12 February 1817 he appeared again at Covent Garden, and after two performances of *Richard III* found himself unjustly accused as an imitator of Edmund Kean. At age twenty-one he was suddenly the center of theatrical gossip and the cause of at least two theater riots. Personally, he seems to have been on good terms with this rival, however, for twice, in February of 1817 and on 7 August 1820, he played Iago to Kean's *Othello*. In January of 1821 Booth married and, traveling by way of France and Madeira, sailed to America with his new bride. On 6 July he made his American debut at Richmond, Virginia, and on 5 October 1821 he appeared at the Park Theatre in New York for the first time. Obviously intending to stay in the New World, he acquired a tract of land near Bel Air, Maryland, where he built a small house and began to raise his family, three of whom, Junius Brutus Junior, Edwin, and John Wilkes, were to make their mark on American history. Aside from short visits to England in 1825 and 1836, his career from 1821 on was an American career. He attained popularity swiftly. Walt Whitman, looking back at the first decade of the Bowery Theatre, which opened in October of 1826, saw it as existing strictly as a showcase for the performances of two actors, Edwin Forrest and Junius Brutus Booth. Being a capable linguist—he spoke German, Dutch, and French and had once played Shylock with a Jewish accent—he may well be the first American actor to perform in any other than his native language. In 1828 while in New Orleans as the stage manager of the Camp Street Theatre he acted Oreste in Racine's *Andromaque* in French at the neighboring Théâtre d'Orléans. In 1831 he assumed for a while the management of the Adelphi Theatre in Baltimore. He began about this time, unfortunately, to exhibit the symptoms of a deranged mind, but he remained a favorite with audiences as far afield as Boston and New Orleans. In Mobile he acted with the young Joseph Jefferson III. In his autobiography, Jefferson tells of Booth's ability to assume and drop his character at will and of performances so intense that the audience was stunned into silence and could not applaud. In 1852 he joined his sons Edwin and Junius Brutus Junior in a tour of California. Leaving them, he traveled eastward and played at the Charles Street Theatre in New Orleans what was to be his final engagement. His last appearance on any stage was on 19 November 1852. He died eleven days later on board a steamboat bound for Cincinnati.

6. Junius Brutus Booth in the title role of John Howard Payne's *Brutus*
by John Neagle, 1827
Oil on canvas, 26 x 15½
Lent by Museum of the City of New York, Theatre and Music Collection

*Manuel del Popolo
Vicente Garcia
1775-1832*

After seventeen years of fame as tenor and composer on the stages of Europe, Manuel Garcia brought Italian opera to America. On 29 November 1825, at the Park Theatre, New York heard for the first time, in the language of the composer, Gioacchino Rossini's perennial favorite *Il Barbiere di Siviglia*. Garcia had created the role of Count Almaviva at the opera's premiere in Rome in 1816 and his gifted daughter, Maria, had made her London debut as Rosina in the same work. The New World's first Italian performance of *Il Barbiere*—it had been heard in New York in 1819 in English—was really a family affair. Manuel Sr. sang Count Almaviva, Maria sang Rosina, Signora Garcia was Berta, and Manuel Jr. had the title role of the barber, Figaro. The enthusiasm of the New York audience must have been more impassioned than reported by Dominick Lynch to the soprano Giuditta Pasta in a letter dated 30 November 1825: "Yesterday evening we had the first Italian opera that has ever been given in America. It was received with enthusiasm . . ." Interest in the foreign language musical theater was at least sufficient to promote two performances a week for nine months. For a while their performances alternated with those of Edmund Kean. What opera lover today does not envy the New Yorkers who heard the Garcias, father and daughter, two of the brightest operatic names of the nineteenth century, in Mozart's *Don Giovanni,* Rossini's *Otello, Tancredi,* and *Il Barbiere,* and the two operas written expressly for Maria by her father, *L'amante Astuto* and *La Figlia dell'aria?* Leaving Maria behind in New York in an ill-fated marriage of convenience to the French banker François Eugéne Malibran, the rest of the troupe went to Mexico. After a profitable tour of eighteen months they returned to Europe, leaving behind in the hands of bandits a reputed 6,000 pounds sterling, which had been the profits of their tour, and in the memories of satisfied audiences a taste for more Italian opera.

7. Manuel Garcia
by an unidentified artist, circa 1800
Oil on canvas, 32 by 22¾
Lent by Boston Museum of Fine Arts. Bequest of John T. Spaulding

Ira Aldridge was the first native-born American actor to win international recognition. Born in New York on 24 July 1807, he probably acted for the first time in the African Theatre on Mercer Street. In 1824 or 1825 he went to England, and billed as "Mr. Keene," his earliest documented appearance on stage occurred as Oroonoko in *The Revolt of Surinam* at London's Royal Coburg Theatre on 10 October 1825. The critics' reviews ran the gamut from praise to ridicule. The writer for the *Times* stated, "It is very difficult to criticize a black actor, on account of the novelty of the spectacle . . . ," and then went on to describe a performance that he said was characterized by "rant and affectation." *The Morning Adviser,* however, found the eighteen-year-old actor's performance "a very excellent conception of the character." On 17 December 1825 Ira Aldridge played Othello for the first time at the Theatre Royal in Brighton, and exactly two years later he had gained sufficient reputation to win his first official international recognition in the form of an honorary commission in the Grenadier Guards of the President of Haiti. The West Indian nation honored him for his London performance in *The Death of Christophe,* a play about the Haitian struggle for independence. In December of 1831 he reached one of the high points of his early career when he was seen in Dublin by Edmund Kean and recommended by him to the manager of the Theatre Royal in Bath. By the Spring of 1833, when he played Othello for the first time at London's Covent Garden on 10 April, he had shed his false name and was now appearing as " Mr. Aldridge,"and as "The African Roscius." He had also acquired the animosity of the pro-slavery group which controlled the managements of the fashionable London West End theaters and was in effect banned from them after his second performance at Covent Garden. For the next nineteen years he stayed primarily in the provinces. Notable successes during these years were his appearances in the title role of *Fabian the Mulatto,* and his own adaptation of Shakespeare's *Titus Andronicus,* purged of all its gore and unpleasantness. It was the first production of the play in 128 years, and Aldridge took the opportunity also to rework the character of Aaron, whom he played, from a black villian to a black hero. On 28 April 1851 he played a performance of *Othello* in the Shakespeare Theatre at Stratford-upon-Avon. By April of 1852 some of the less prejudiced critics of the London press were calling him "a star of the first magnitude." In July of 1852 he left for his first tour of the Continent. Except for a short engagement at the Haymarket Theatre in London in the Summer of 1865 he was never again to act in England. From his first appearance in Europe until his last he was passionately received by all who saw him. The *Preussische Zeitung* called him, after seeing his Othello, "the most beautiful male artist that one can imagine . . ." and the famous French critic Théophile Gautier, having seen him in St. Petersburg, described his acting as "a majestically classical style much resembling that of Macready," and considered his King Lear, one of

8. Ira Aldridge in the title role of Shakespeare's *Othello*
by Henry Perronet Briggs, circa 1826
Oil on canvas, 48 x 40
Lent by Garrick Club, London

the roles he played in "white-face," an even better performance than his famed Othello. Frederick William IV presented him with the gold medal of the Prussian Academy of Arts and Sciences, an award made previously only to Baron von Humboldt, Franz Liszt, and the composer Gasparo Spontini. He was knighted by Duke Bernhard of Saxe-Meiningen, given the White Cross of Switzerland by the city of Berne, and among other honors was granted an honorary membership in the Imperial Academy of Beaux Arts of Russia where he was a special favorite of audiences and fellow actors from 1858 on. In March of 1866 he became the first actor to perform Shakespeare in English in Constantinople. He was planning a tour of America when he died at Lodz, Poland, on 7 August 1867. He was buried there with full civil and military honors and his grave is now cared for by the Society of Polish Artists of Film and Theatre.

Edwin Forrest's first attempts at theatricals were made on the stage of the South Street Theatre in his native Philadelphia when he was eleven years old. His professional debut was made only three years later, on 27 November 1820, in the same city's Walnut Street Theatre; he then served an apprenticeship in small theaters on the frontier, playing in towns along the Ohio and Mississippi rivers as far south as New Orleans. In 1825 he was acting in Albany where he played Iago to Edmund Kean's Othello. On 23 June 1826, with an audacity that was very much part of his nature, he made his New York debut in the Park Theatre playing the role that had been Kean's the season before. He was a great success and was hired by the Bowery Theatre where his characterizations and his vigorous manner of declamation endeared him to the downtown audiences. After five seasons at the Bowery, Forrest was engaged by the Park Theatre. While there, he encouraged the writing of plays with American subjects, offering prizes to their authors. Both John A. Stone's *Metamora,* first produced on 15 December 1829, and Robert M. Bird's *The Gladiator,* premiered on 15 September 1831, were to remain among the most popular of Forrest's stage creations throughout his career. In 1834 he retired temporarily from the stage in his native land to travel in Europe and to make his London debut. His strong personality and the passion of his acting won for him there, also, enthusiastic audiences, and he became the first American to achieve success both in his native country and abroad. He also took time out from the rigors of recreation and of profession to fall in love and to marry Catharine Norton Sinclair in the English capital on 23 June 1837. Fittingly, the clergyman presiding at the marriage was Henry Hart Milman, author of the melodrama *Fazio,* a play beloved on both sides of the Atlantic. In 1845 Forrest visited England for the second time. Ill received by hissing claques during a London appearance as Macbeth he comprehended the incident as the work of his English rival William Charles Macready and returned the favor by hissing the British actor at a performance of *Hamlet* in Edinburgh on 2 March 1846. Forrest then arrogantly admitted the action in a letter submitted to the London *Times* and began a controversy which was to culminate in New York in the Astor Place Riot of 10 May 1849. Forrest's reputation was sullied by the affair, but he remained in favor with those audiences which saw him as a champion of native Americanism. Two years later his

Continued on page 34

9. Edwin Forrest as Rolla in Thomas Brinsley Sheridan's adaption of A. F. F. von Kotzebue's *Pizarro*
by John Neagle, 1826
Oil on canvas, 26 x 22
Lent by Edwin Forrest Home

name was again paraded by the press for offstage performances when he and his wife sued each other for divorce. From 1852 on he frequently went into self-imposed retirement. In 1860 he reappeared with great success in New York and Boston as Hamlet, and in 1866, although laboring with partial paralysis, he played to record audiences in Chicago and San Francisco. His last appearance was in Boston on 7 December 1872. Upon his death in Philadelphia five days later, it was discovered that he had left his entire estate for the founding of a home for retired actors.

10. Edwin Forrest in the title role of John Augustus Stone's *Metamora*
by Frederick Styles Agate, circa 1830
Oil on canvas, 24½ x 19½
From the collection of the National Portrait Gallery

William Charles Macready
1793-1873

During the sixteen years he had appeared on English stages prior to his first appearance in New York's Park Theatre on 2 October 1826, William Charles Macready had risen slowly and steadily to the highest rank of his profession. Playbills announced him as "That Eminent Tragedian" and despite a reputation among his colleagues for unpleasantness and egotism he was a favorite with critics and public alike. The completeness of his characterizations and the evenness of his performance from first curtain to last came as a welcome relief from the usual bombastic declamation of his time. During his first American tour he was being paid twice what his presence commanded at London's Drury Lane, and by the time he acted his last performance of *Macbeth* at the Park on 4 June 1827, he had amassed both considerable reputation and profit from his new audiences. He returned to England considering eventual retirement in this promising New World. He returned again in September of 1843 for a second American tour. This time around his success was dampened by the growing hostility of Edwin Forrest. His audiences still appreciated his efforts, however, and he went home thirteen months later 5,500 pounds richer than when he had come. On 4 October 1848, he began a farewell tour of the United States with a performance of *Macbeth* at Niblo's Astor Place Opera House in New York. One of the Boston newspapers had greeted him viciously upon his arrival for this tour, and he unwisely made a curtain speech in reply to the attack. It was taken as a challenge by the overly chauvinistic members of The Native American political party and by Edwin Forrest's staunchest fans who included among their number many disreputable Bowery types. Toward the end of his farewell tour, Macready appeared again at the Astor Place on 7 May 1849. Abuse and chairs from the gallery rained down on him and Macready was forced to terminate the performance. Placated by a visiting committee of New York supporters, he attempted to act again three days later. An unruly mob of ten to fifteen thousand assembled outside the theater along with sizeable detachments from the New York police and militia. In the inevitable riot which ensued about thirty people were killed. Macready was forced to flee the city in disguise, although his role in the disgraceful affair had merely been that of innocent catalyst. He returned to England having discarded any idea of retiring in the United States and was convinced, as were many others, of Edwin Forrest's disgraceful importance as an instigator, if not the mastermind, of the disastrous Astor Place Riot.

11. William Macready in the title role of James Sheridan Knowle's *William Tell* by Henry Inman, circa 1827
Oil on canvas, 30¼ x 25
Lent by the Metropolitan Museum of Art, Rogers Fund, 1906

Clara Fisher
1811–1898

Clara Fisher began her professional career at age six on the stage of London's Drury Lane Theatre, appearing in both the play *Lilliput* and part of the fifth act of *Richard III*. She toured throughout England as a child actress and spent three years as a member of the professional company at the Drury Lane just prior to her coming to America. Her debut at New York's Park Theatre in 1827 was as Albina Mandeville in a play called *The Will*. The ballad "Hurrah for the Bonnets of Blue" which she introduced into the play to enliven her part had electrifying effect upon her audience and was forever associated with her. As a young and pretty actress she was well received, and women young and old who thought themselves fashionable imitated her hair style and her lisp. She was painted by both Chester Harding and Henry Inman; the second artist portrayed her wearing her armlet mounted with a miniature of George Frederick Cooke. Although she seems to have had a rather limited vocal range, she ventured into opera with pleasing results. Her singing of John Howard Payne's "Home, Sweet Home" in Sir Henry Bishop's musical setting from his opera *Clari; or The Maid of Milan* was one of those magical moments in the history of the theater that always moved audiences to tears. In 1834 she married James Gaspard Maeder, vocal coach of the visiting English singers Mary Ann and Joseph Wood. As "Mrs. Maeder" she appeared on opera bills throughout the country. At one significant performance in Boston on 8 April 1835 she sang Susanna in a production of Mozart's *The Marriage of Figaro* that marked the stage debut of a young local singer named Charlotte Cushman. In a manner of gilding the lily typical of the times, the Mozart was topped off with a performance of a comic opera called *Pet of the Petticoats* with Mrs. Maeder in the role of Poll the Pet. Mrs. Maeder's popularity waned with her youth, but she remained on the American stage for sixty years, playing roles ranging from light comedy to Shakespearian tragedy. In 1843, with the cooperation of John Sefton, she introduced musical theatricals in the Boston Museum, and in the Fall of 1845 she was one of the first members of the stock company of Boston's Howard Athenaeum. She also continued to appear on the New York stage, one notable occasion being the 1865 performance of *School for Scandal* which opened Lucy Rushton's Theatre. Clara Fisher Maeder's last appearance on stage was in Baltimore in 1889 as Mrs. Jeremiah Joblots in Augustin Daly's *Lottery of Love*. She died in Metuchen, New Jersey, at the home of her daughter-in-law on 12 November 1898.

12. Clara Fisher
by Henry Inman, 1828
Oil on canvas, 30 x 25
Lent by Indianapolis Museum of Arts, gift of Mrs. John E. Fehsenfeld

Fanny Kemble
1809–1893

As the heiress to the talent of one of England's leading theatrical families—she was the niece of John Philip Kemble and Sarah Siddons and the daughter of Charles Kemble—Fanny Kemble made her debut onstage when her family needed her. She made her first appearance as Juliet at Covent Garden 5 October 1829 in a successful effort to save her father from financial ruin. She never liked acting and she was rather condescending in her attitude toward most in her profession. On 18 September 1832 she appeared for the first time in the United States when she acted Bianca in Henry Hart Milman's *Fazio* at the Park Theatre in New York. Although her manner offstage was quite often haughty and her performances onstage were uneven, she charmed her American audiences sufficiently to be an immediate and grand success. Although it gave much more coverage to the Italian opera then popular in the City of Brotherly Love, and to Edwin Forrest's exploits at the Arch Street Theatre, the *United States Gazette* prepared Philadelphia for her debut in that city by quoting reviews as early as two days after her first performance in New York: "The New York Enquirer of yesterday says—Miss Fanny Kemble made her first appearance last evening. . . . As an actress she stands unrivalled before the American public; and never have we seen one who can compare with her." By the time she finally appeared in Philadelphia the theater-going public was well disposed to receive her with open arms. After her performance as Belvedera in *Venice Preserved* the correspondent of the *Gazette* wrote on 24 October 1832, "It was the first opportunity we have had to view the latter (Fanny) in Tragedy, and, to us, her offerings at the shrine of Melpomene, were more acceptable than those presented to her gay laughter-loving sister." Her Bianca was again admired as was her Julia in *The Hunchback*. Her Washington debut was attended by Dolley Madison and John Quincy Adams. John Marshall and Joseph Story came often to see her while she was in the capital, and she was even presented to President Jackson at the White House. In Philadelphia she had met an eligible young—and rich—bachelor named Pierce Butler. He presistently followed her on her tours, sometimes playing the flute in theater orchestras to be near her. She eventually succumbed to his wooing and on 7 June 1834 they were married in Philadelphia's Christ Church. It was the end of her short career in America, for two weeks later she acted her farewell performance in the aptly chosen *The Wedding Day* at the Chestnut Street Theatre. Her married life, however, was not happy, and she left her husband and returned to England. In February of 1847 she went back again to the stage, but as before, she found it distasteful. The following spring she held her first readings of Shakespeare from a lecture platform. Finding this method of reaching her audiences less objectionable than assuming a character in costume, it was how she chose to appear in public until her last public reading in 1869. Her husband having died in 1867, Fanny spent the remainder of her life visiting with daughters in England and Germantown, Pennsylvania. She died in London on 15 January 1893.

13. Fanny Kemble as Bianca in Henry Hart Milman's *Fazio*
by Thomas Sully, 1833
Oil on canvas, 30 x 25½
Lent by Pennsylvania Academy of Fine Arts

Mary Ann Wood
1802-1864

When Mary Ann Wood made her American debut at the Park Theatre in New York as Cinderella on 19 September 1833, she had already held title for some years to the claim of being one of England's finest singers. In 1822, at age nineteen, she was fully established professionally when she appeared at London's Covent Garden as Mandane in Arne's opera *Artaxerxes*. In the United States she will always be associated with the role of Amina in Vincenzo Bellini's opera *La Sonnambula*. She and her tenor husband, Joseph Wood, first introduced it to the American public in New York, in English, during the early part of the season of 1835-1836. They repeated the opera eleven times with great success in Boston—where Mrs. Wood also found time to encourage a young singer named Charlotte Cushman—and then brought it to Philadelphia. Here, the *United States Gazette* ran a laudatory column on 11 February 1836, the day scheduled for the first performance. We do not know who the author of the column may have been, but if he was not a public relations man in the pay of the Woods he certainly should have been. Two short excerpts suffice to show off his talent:

An Italian, who was the personal friend of Bellini, thus writes from Boston:—'Last night I went to hear La Sonnambula by Bellini!—which I heard at home, two days before I went away. Mrs. Wood sings it like an angel (come un'angelo!) she sings and acts it with her soul. She would astonish, delight, and make crazy, an Italian audience. Per Dio! che musica! and what singing!' . . . If, then, gentle reader, thou wouldst enjoy an elevating pastime, and refresh thyself with a refining pleasure, go and hear La Sonnambula. If thou art old, the dreams of youth will again come o'er thee—if thou art young, the depth and sanctity of thy feelings will be revealed to thee,—if thou are care-worn, tranquility will visit thy weary breast; if thou art immersed in the world's business, better moments will cheer thee;—if thou hast a human heart, and would have its fountains stirred, and thy spirit soothed, agitated and renewed—go—go—gentle reader—go and hear La Sonnambula.

So great was the response of the Philadelphia music-loving public that the opera was performed every night but Sunday from the eleventh until the twenty-sixth of February. The future of Romantic opera in America was assured by this remarkable marathon of bel canto singing. It should be noted, however, that to make certain the audience went away satisfied, each night's performance of the opera was capped with lighter entertainment. Let us hope that those who did not succumb to the pathos of *Sonnambula* did at least enjoy the performances of those timeless favorites *Freaks and Follies*, *Forty Winks,* and *The Twa Ghaists*. Mary Ann Wood appeared intermittently in this country until 1841, quite frequently to the tune of her husband's business disagreements with various theater managers. The Wood's last appearance here was in a production of Bellini's *Norma* in an English translation by Joseph R. Fry. It opened at Philadelphia's Chestnut Street Theatre on 11 January 1841 and was sung for the last time on 4 February. Four days later the Woods sailed for England vowing in a press announcement never to return.

14. Mary Ann Wood as Amina in Vincenzo Bellini's *La Sonnambula*
by John Neagle, 1836
Oil on canvas, 30 x 25
Lent by Hirschl and Adler Galleries

Charlotte Cushman
1816-1876

Charlotte Cushman was an eighteen-year-old contralto in the choir of Ralph Waldo Emerson's Boston church when the visiting English prima donna Mary Ann Wood encouraged her to pursue a career in grand opera. Consequently, Charlotte made her debut on 8 April 1835 as the Countess Almaviva in Mozart's *The Marriage of Figaro* at Boston's Tremont Theatre. By December of that year she was appearing with a touring opera company in New Orleans. It was here her singing career came to an ungracious end. Either because she had been pushed into soprano roles too uncomfortable for her natural contralto voice, or because she had been singing too strenuously without proper coaching, the early bloom of her voice was gone. The kindest of the New Orleans critics was certainly the one who suggested she should spare the public and limit herself to non-singing roles. On 23 April 1836 she made her dramatic debut at the St. Charles Theatre in no less a starring role than that of Lady Macbeth. She was an immediate success and her career as America's greatest actress of the century was begun. That it happened to be Shakespeare's birthday was indeed a good omen for her. Her debut at New York's Bowery Theatre came in September of 1836, and in May of the following year, with an ever-growing entourage of enthusiastic fans to applaud her efforts, she first appeared as Meg Merrilies in *Guy Mannering*. The effect she created as the old gypsy hag was from all reports one of the most outstanding characterizations on the nineteenth-century stage. In February of 1845 she made her London debut at the Princess Theatre as Bianca in Milman's *Fazio*. Her reputation grew steadily as she acted in England in *Othello* with Edwin Forrest, and in *Macbeth* with William Macready, and held her own against both these formidable stage personalities. She was not exactly beloved by the latter when the London papers compared Charlotte's "fiery eloquence" to his "measured emotions and frigid mannerisms." She played Romeo there for the first time in 1846. Being not the

Continued on page 46

15. Charlotte Cushman
by an unidentified artist, circa 1836
Oil on canvas, 23¾ x 18½
Lent by Mrs. Edward M. Pflueger

[44]

most feminine of actresses, she reveled in the so-called "trouser roles" and took justifiable pride in her acting of Oberon, Cardinal Wolsey, and Hamlet, as well as Juliet's teenage lover. In 1849 she returned triumphantly to the United States acclaimed as an international success and hailed as "Our Charlotte." By 15 May 1852 she had decided to retire from the stage at the height of her popularity and acted Meg Merrilies as her "farewell" to New York. She had the good sense, however, to know when to interrupt her "retirement" to alleviate her boredom and accelerate her finances. After only two years of residence in Rome she was back on the London stage. During the season of 1857 and 1858 she acted again in the United States and, although the country was in the midst of a depression, her box-office intake broke records everywhere she appeared. Then home again to Rome. She became almost a commuter across the Atlantic. She was in the United States in 1860 and 1863, when she aided the American Sanitary Commission by acting a series of benefits for Civil War relief. A trip in 1868 involved only personal business and no acting. When not traveling she was at home in Rome where she played host to the leading American and English literati who frequented the Eternal City. She mothered a small tribe of relatives and female protégés and signed her notes to them "Big Mama." In 1870 she returned to the United States for the last time and kept busy on her beloved stage almost until the time of her death. She acted at Booth's Theatre in New York for forty-two nights beginning 25 September 1871, and the engagement brought in an unprecedented $57,000. Late in 1872 she began a career as a reader. Her last stage appearance was as Lady Macbeth at Booth's Theatre on 7 November 1874. As a tribute to America's greatest tragedian the curtain was rung down immediately after the famous "Sleepwalking Scene"—exactly as had been done at the farewell of her illustrious English predecessor Sarah Siddons. She died in Boston on 18 February 1876.

16. Charlotte Cushman
by William Page, 1853
Oil on canvas, 27½ x 22
Lent by Charles Van Brunt Cushman

Born Augusta Williams, it was under the name of her actor-manager stepfather Robert Campbell Maywood that America's first internationally famous dancer achieved professional renown. After instruction by the Philadelphia dancing teachers Madame and Monsieur Paul Hazard, Augusta Maywood made her debut in that city's Chestnut Street Theatre on 30 December 1837, dancing the role of Zelica in *The Maid of Cashmere*. Ably promoted by her stepfather—who at this point was manager of the theatre—she became an overnight sensation, not only in her home city, but also in New York where she made her Park Theatre debut on 12 February 1838. Sometime later, "La Petite Augusta," as she was called on playbills and in the press, sailed for France to complete her dance education with Jean Coralli in the ballet school of the Paris Opéra. On 11 November 1839 she made her Opéra debut dancing a pas de deux with Charles Mabille in the first act of her teacher's ballet *Le Diable boiteux*. The critics received her with great praise, and she was engaged by the Opéra for a year at a salary of 3,000 francs. Her career in Paris ended when she eloped with Charles Mabille almost exactly one year from the date of her debut. The newly married couple danced together in France for several years and then during the season of 1843–1844 appeared at the Theatro de São Carlos in Lisbon. In 1845 Augusta deserted her husband and resumed dancing under her own name. She was never to return to Paris but went on to great fame in other European dance capitals. In 1845 she was declared prima ballerina at Vienna's Hofbergoperntheater where she was one of the first to demand, and achieve, equal billing with famous guest artists. In 1848 she was engaged for the first time by Milan's Teatro de la Scala. With the great Austrian ballerina Fanny Elssler she alternated dancing the lead role in the premiere performances of Jules Perrot's great ballet *Faust* and also shared, as incongruous as it seems, the title of "prima ballerina e prima mima assoluta." About this time she became one of the first dancers to organize and travel with a semipermanent company, joining with Giuseppe and Giovanni Battista Lasina to create a notable company that toured Italy during one of that country's great eras of dance. Except for one return engagement in Vienna in 1854, Augusta Maywood devoted the remainder of her career to dancing in Italy. When one reads the comments that Italian journalists made about her such as, "queen of the air," "new Terpsichore," and "incomparable both as mime and dancer," there is no doubt of her celebrity. She appeared in works by Italy's leading choreographers, one of the most interesting—from an American point of view—Giuseppe Rota's *I bianchi ed i negri,* which premiered in Milan on 10 November 1853. One year after its first publication in Italian, here is *Uncle Tom's Cabin* danced as a ballet in Milan. Although records are incomplete, it is presumed that Augusta Maywood danced Little Eva. In 1856 she danced for the first time Filippo Termanini's *Rita Gauthier,* a role that became associated particularly with her and although a trifle, one she danced frequently until the end of her career, althernating it with masterpieces such as Perrot's *Faust* and *Esmeralda*. She danced for the last time in 1859 and opened a school of ballet in Vienna. Her death occurred from smallpox in what is now the city of Lvov, Poland, on 3 November 1876.

17. Augusta Maywood in the title role of the ballet *Rita Gauthier*
Drawn by Aug. Bedetti, printed by Pieroni, Ancona, Italy, 1856
Lithograph on paper, 23¾ x 16½
Lent by Parmenia Migel Ekstrom

Ato I° nel Ballo Rita Gauthier

Ant.º BEDETTI dis.   Lit. F.ª PIERONI Ancona

AUGUSTA MAYWOOD

nella Primavera del 1856 in Ancona

Noi ti vedemmo e cesammo	Che modi, AUGUSTA, e il plauso
Il nostro plauso avesti	Udrai concorde ancora,
Il movoggiamo, e sempre	Chela magia del ballo
Novello ardor tu desti	E d'esser nuovo agnora.

Paul Taglioni
1808–1884

Amalia Taglioni
1801–1881

The ballet *La Sylphide,* with choreography by Filippo Taglioni and music by Jean Schneitzhoeffer, was first performed in Paris in 1832 and marked the beginning of the Romantic Age of the Dance. Fragments of the ballet had been performed in the United States from 1835 on, and its first complete performance was given in New York's Park Theatre on 22 May 1839. The occasion was the American debut of Paul Taglioni, son of the choreographer, and his wife, Amalia Galster Taglioni. Paul Taglioni had acquired a notable reputation as a dancer and ballet master, and since he and his wife were among the first European dancers of note to come to the United States, it is understandable that they were well received. Three days after their debut, the New York *Literary Gazette* reported that "Madame Taglioni is remarkable for the peculiar ease, as well as the grace and elegance of her movements; many of her figures and steps are entirely new to a New York audience," and of her husband: "Nor is Mons. Taglioni less excellent in his art—perhaps, of the two, he is the best dancer; a symmetrical figure adds greatly to the pleasure which his performance gives; he is entirely free from the buffoonery which generally distinguishes male dancers of the French ballet . . ." The Taglionis were in this country for only five months. After their May performances in New York they appeared in Philadelphia, took a July vacation to Niagara Falls, and closed their American engagement by appearing again at the Park in August and September. On 2 October 1839 they took ship for London. During their relatively short stay they had firmly planted one of the most important and durable ballet classics in American taste and had sowed seeds of enthusiasm for the dance, which were to blossom less than a year later with the arrival of Fanny Elssler.

18. Paul Taglioni as James and Amalia Taglioni in the title role of *La Sylphide*
Published by H. R. Robinson, New York, 1839
Lithograph, trimmed to 8¹¹⁄₁₆ x 13, hand colored
Lent by Cia Fornaroli Collection, Dance Collection, The New York Public Library

[50]

Lith of H.R.Robinson, 52 Courtlandt St. N.Y.

MONS. PAUL TAGLIONI.   MADAME TAGLIONI.

In the Characters of La Sylphide & James Reuben, at the Park-Theatre, New-York, May 22d 1839.
Principal Dancers of the Opera House.

Mary Ann Lee
1823-1899

As early as age eleven Mary Ann Lee was playing various children's roles on the Philadelphia stage, but she made her official debut as a dancer on 30 December 1837 as Fatima in *The Maid of Cashmere* when she was twelve or thirteen. Her rival in the small company of the Chestnut Street Theatre was twelve-year-old Augusta Maywood, who was later to go on to fame in Europe. In September of the following year Mary Ann transferred her allegiance to the Walnut Street Theatre where she danced the new ballet, *The Lily Queen,* produced especially for her. Between dances she acted Albert in support of Edwin Forrest's William Tell. In April of 1839 Mary Ann's success as Zoloe in the ballet *La Bayadere* led to her engagement by the Bowery Theatre in New York where she made her debut on June 12 in the same work. There on 8 July she danced the Cachucha for President James Van Buren. She appeared at P. T. Barnum's Vauxhall Gardens and to further her career studied with Fanny Elssler's partner James Sylvain while the famed Viennese prima ballerina was appearing at the Park Theatre. To the delight of the nationalists in her audience she dared dance the Cachucha at Vauxhall while Elssler was performing it at the Park. After a tour of the United States, which took her as far afield as New Orleans and Mobile, she went off to Paris from November of 1844 until September of 1845 to study with the staff of the ballet at the Opéra. Her progress in her studies was eagerly followed by American fans of ballet, and she made a triumphant second debut in *La Jolie Fille du Gand* at Philadelphia's Arch Street Theatre on 24 November 1845. One month later she began a tour with a company she had newly organized around herself, and in Boston on 1 January 1846, with George Washington Smith as her Albrecht, she performed the first American production of the now venerable and perennial favorite *Giselle.* We have no review of that premiere, but of a performance at the Park Theatre on 14 April 1846, the correspondent of the *New York Herald* commented: ". . . Miss Lee enacted Giselle with beauty, charm, elegance and grace that cannot be described, and we will not attempt it . . ." What was the pinnacle of her career became the climax, for during her tour of 1846–1847 her health began to fail, and she was obliged to dance her farewell performance on the stage of the Arch Street Theatre on 18 June 1847. None but the most vehement of her followers would have claimed she was the equal of Fanny Elssler and the other noted European dancers who were exhibiting their virtuosity to American audiences at that time. She was admired everywhere, however, as the best American ballerina of her time, and one whose charming stage personality and presence drew sympathetic and enthusiastic audiences, What height of greatness she might have achieved as a dancer these audiences would never know—for she was forced to retire at age twenty-four. She died in 1899.

19. Mary Ann Lee in the dance *La Smolenska*
B. W. Thayer & Co. Lithography
Published by William H. Oakes, Boston, 1842
Lithograph, 7¾ x 4½
Lent by Dance Collection, The New York Public Library.

LA SMOLENSKA.

as danced by

G.W. Thayer & Co's Lithog.y Boston.

Price 25 cts. net

MISS MARY ANN LEE.

BOSTON.

Published by WM. H. OAKES, and sold by

JOHN ASHTON & Co. 197 Washington St.

Entered according to act of Congress in the year 1846 by W.H. Oakes in the Clerks office of the District Court of Massachusetts.

Fanny Elssler was twenty-nine years old and near the peak of her career when Stephan Price, co-manager of the Park Theatre, met her in Paris in the autumn of 1839 and persuaded her to contract for her first American appearances. Left the sole proprietor of the Park by Price's death some months later, Edmund Simpson almost canceled the contract for fear that she would be received with little enthusiasm and with loss rather than profit. He could not have been more wrong. Being the first European ballerina to contemplate a tour of America, Fanny Elssler was eagerly awaited. The New York press, notably the *New York Morning Herald,* paved the way to her New World success with glittering reviews of her personal accomplishments and her professional triumphs. The first issue of the *Spirit of the Times,* published after her Park Theatre debut on 14 May 1840, described in the florid prose of the period the scene when she appeared onstage, "The celebrated dance of *La Cracovienne* followed, and brought the fair *debutante* before the public at a bound! The time-honored walls of Old Drury never echoed with more tumultuous, deafening plaudits. The pit rose *en masse*—hats and handkerchiefs waved in every direction." And after she had danced her second number of the evening, the ballet *La Tarentule,* "she was called for with a degree of enthusiasm unprecedented in the theatrical annals of this country." The mass hysteria that began that night in New York was to follow her through most of her appearances during her twenty-six-month tour of the United States and Cuba. Philadelphia saw her for the first time a month later and, among other honors paid her, produced a cast-metal candelabra base depicting her in the costume of her famed Spanish dance, *La Cachucha.* On 11 July 1840 she appeared for the first time in Washington, and Congress adjourned early so that its members could be in attendance. Having attended her third performance in the capital city in the company of his entire Cabinet, President Martin Van Buren invited her to the White House the following morning. Tongues wagged at the disgrace of a dancer being received at the White House. In Baltimore she was at first coolly received, but after her second performance the horses were unharnessed from her carriage and jubilant male fans drew carriage and their new idol to her hotel. Boston was determined not to follow the example of the other cities, but soon capitulated to her talent and her personality. Emerson and Longfellow were charmed by her. Half the city found her benefit for the Bunker Hill Monument Fund a gracious response to their hospitality, while the other half expressed indignation that the earnings of a foreign ballet dancer should be so used. Richmond was more appreciative when she agreed to dance an unscheduled performance there. The Governor of Virginia escorted her on a visit to the state capitol and she was borne there from her hotel on a litter carried on the shoulders of six state senators. When she first appeared in Havana in January of 1841 she was paid the unprecedented sum of $1,000 a night. In April she appeared in New Orleans where wreaths of strawberries joined the usual wreaths of flowers flung onstage at the end of a performance. The second year of her tour was spoiled slightly by malicious stories about her in the press, but she went on her triumphant peregrination of American theaters as the queen she

20. Fanny Elssler
by Henry Inman, 1841
Oil on canvas, 23¾ x 27¾
Lent by Haydn Museum, Eisenstadt, Austria

was. By the end of her tour she had danced 208 performances and had supposedly earned nearly $140,000. Much of this was given to charity. Her last performance in America, a benefit for the Theatrical Fund, was danced at the Park Theatre on 1 July 1842. She sailed for Europe from New York on 16 July, on board the *Caledonia*. As the steamer left the harbor the band in the ship-of-the-line *Ohio* played "America" and "La Cracovienne" in farewell. Fanny Elssler danced for the last time in Vienna on 21 June 1851 and died there on 27 November 1884.

Jenny Lind
1820-1887

Jenny Lind was twenty-eight years old when she retired from the operatic stage in May of 1849. She had been the darling of Europe for eleven years, rating ovations and rewards greater than those paid to any previous soprano. Even Queen Victoria herself attended all of Jenny's performances during her farewell engagement in London. She had not, however, given up the concert stage and so when P. T. Barnum's agent caught up with her in Lübeck, Germany, in January of 1850, she signed a contract to appear in America. Her debut was prepared with all the masterful showmanship that Barnum could muster, and as soon as she appeared on the dock at New York on the first Sunday in September 1850 a wave of mass hysteria began to roll before she had even sung a note. Items of clothing and furniture were named for her, and her likeness appeared in thousands of lithographs and on glass bottles and tobacco labels. To heighten the excitement Barnum had hit upon the idea of auctioning off the tickets to the first concert in each city where she would appear. In New York a hatter named Genin—who just happened to be a friend of Barnum—won the first ticket for $225. Providence and Philadelphia buyers were later to shame him by paying $650 and $625, respectively. During rehearsal for her first American concert at New York's Castle Garden on 11 September 1850, Jenny had no sooner begun to sing when she was interrupted by a one-hundred gun salute celebrating the admission of California to the Union. She took it as a good omen. Her debut concert, which opened with the "Casta Diva" from Bellini's *Norma* and ended with a saccharine piece called "Welcome to America" written especially for the occasion by Julius Benedict to a prize-winning text by Bayard Taylor, was notable not only for the artistry of the singing and the applause, but for several innovations in theater management. Barnum, correctly predicting an immense sellout audience, had color-coded the auditorium and the tickets to make seating simpler and had used detachable ticket stubs for the first time. As was so often her practice in Europe, where her piety and generosity endeared her to monarchs and subjects alike, she gave her $10,000 share of the first-night proceeds to charity. Throughout the rest of her ninety-three-concert tour under Barnum's management Jenny Lind became even more of a national sensation. Daniel Webster and Henry Wadsworth Longfellow came to pay their respects to her in Boston and in Washington where a new hall was being built just for her first appearance there—it was, of course, not finished on time—Millard Fillmore called on her in her quarters. She was not in, so she later graciously returned the call at the White House. The Philadelphia audience, upholding their reputation as the hardest to please in the nation, gave her a cool reception when she first appeared on stage but was cheering with as much frenzy as the rest of the nation by the end of the first half of the concert. By the time she had made her grand tour and returned to Philadelphia on 9 May 1851 for her last concert under Barnum management, the wily impresario had pocketed $535,486 in box-office receipts while his "Swedish Nightingale" had personally earned another $176,675. Leaving Barnum's flamboyant, but lucrative management, she embarked upon a forty-concert tour of her own and found that the American audiences who had

21. Jenny Lind
by Eduard Magnus, replica circa 1861 of the life portrait of 1846
Oil on canvas, 46½ x 37½
Lent by National Portrait Gallery, London

adored her for the past eight months were turning fickle. Critics found her new accompanist, Otto Goldschmidt, too formal and too dull and they began to hint at Jenny's pigheadedness and temperament. The tour was not a complete loss, however, for she married Goldschmidt in Boston on 5 February 1852. Her last American concert was sung at Castle Garden on 24 May 1852, and five days later Mr. and Mrs. Goldschmidt took ship for England. As Jenny Goldschmidt she concertized until her final performance in Händel's *Messiah* in Düsseldorf in 1866. In 1883, at the request of the Prince of Wales, she became the First Professor of Singing at London's new Royal College of Music. She died in her English country home on 2 November 1887 and was buried, as she had requested, with a shawl given her by Queen Victoria and a patchwork quilt presented to her by children during her American tour.

Although he spoke English with an accent and wrote his personal journal in French, Louis Moreau Gottschalk was born an American and was the first musician and composer of his nation to win international acclaim. Having shown an obvious talent for music as early as age three, he was sent to Paris from his native New Orleans for musical training in May of 1842. By the time of his public debut in Paris on 17 April 1849 he had won praise for his playing from such eminent musicians as Frédéric Chopin and had electrified European musical circles with his own compositions based upon the Afro-Caribbean melodies of his native Louisiana. His was an unqualified success during concert tours of France, Switzerland, and Spain in the years 1845 to 1852. Early in 1853 he returned to the United States and made his New York debut in Niblo's ballrooms on 17 February 1853. In 1854 and 1855 he played in Cuba, while at home his compositions, especially "The Last Hope," became favorites on every parlor piano. In 1857 he was again in the West Indies. His first public appearance in Havana was with a concert group that included the fourteen-year-old soprano Adelina Patti. In February of 1862 he was again back in New York and played the first in a series of concerts which took him on a hectic tour north to Canada and south as far as Norfolk. In several towns he seems to have introduced an extraordinary novelty for the time—a solo concert, one performer unassisted by singers or other instrumentalists. While a few of the more astute critics complained that he did not play enough of the classics, most of his listeners applauded his programs heavy with his own works and transcriptions of operatic arias and ensembles. He was, however, undoubtedly a great musician, and of his own virtuoso playing the critics were constant with descriptive phrases such as "cascade of pearls," "golden touch," and "star dust." In September of 1865 he sailed for South America where he found his most enthusiastic audiences. He played to great acclaim and arranged music festivals and "monster concerts" such as that held in Rio on 24 November 1869, when he led 650 musicians before an enthralled audience that included the royal family of Brazil. The grand finale was a work he had written for the occasion and dedicated to the Emperor, *Marcha Solemne Brasileira.* It had battle effects sounded by backstage cannon. His health had been failing for some time and the following day during another, but less monumental concert, he collapsed and was carried from the stage. He died in Rio on 18 December 1869. Throngs mourned him and in eulogies he was called "the son of free America" and it was noted that "as artist he honored his native land, the United States."

22. Louis Moreau Gottschalk
by Jules or Jean Paul Franceschi, after 1869 from a life mask
Marble, 34 inches high
Lent by New Orleans Public Library

GOTTSCHALK

When he was born near Bel Air, Maryland, on 13 November 1833, Junius Brutus Booth named his fourth son for his friend Edwin Forrest. Young Edwin accompanied his father on theatrical tours from a very early date and his responsibility for his father's increasingly erratic behavior forced on him a grave and melancholy temperament that was never to leave him. Young Edwin made his first appearance on stage at the Boston Museum as Tressel in *Richard III,* 10 September 1849. Two years later he made his debut in a major role when he had to assume the title role in the same work upon his father's indisposition. Edwin accompanied his father and brother Junius Brutus, Jr., to California in 1852. The elder Booth left California sometime later and died on the trip home. Edwin, now on his own, acted for a while in California and Nevada and in 1854 embarked upon a tour to Australia where, in Sydney, he acted Shylock for the first time. On the return trip home he stopped for two months in Honolulu where he produced *Richard III* in the presence of King Kamehameha IV. Booth appeared with increasing popularity in San Francisco and Sacramento, and when he returned to the East Coast he was an experienced and accomplished actor, especially skillful in tragic and highly dramatic roles. He made a spectacular success in Boston in April of 1857 as Sir Giles Overreach in *The Iron Chest* and later in the same year won the approbation of New York audiences for performances in *Richard III* and *Othello.* His Iago in the latter play was especially admired. His tour in England in 1861 was moderately unsuccessful. For the next three years he was seen principally at the Winter Garden Theatre in New York, which for a while he managed. It was there in 1864 that he gave his unprecedented one-hundred-night run of *Hamlet,* a role in which he was particularly successful since it fitted his own temperament so well. His melancholy was compounded when his younger brother John Wilkes Booth assassinated Abraham Lincoln in Washington on that dreadfully misnamed Good Friday in 1865. Although threats had been made on Edwin's life as a result of the murder, he returned to the stage and to generally appreciative audiences at the Winter Garden on 3 January 1866. The theater burned in March of the following year and he immediately planned a building to replace it. Booth's Theatre opened on 3 February 1869 and from then until the season of 1873–1874, when the economic panic in the country forced Booth into bankruptcy, it was the scene of the most notable theatricals that this country had known. Upon Edwin Forrest's death late in 1872 Booth was acknowledged as America's leading actor. In 1878 he had published the annotated text of fifteen of his most frequently performed productions under the title

23. Edwin Booth as Iago in Shakespeare's *Othello* (Frontispiece)
by Thomas Hicks, 1863
Oil on canvas, 31½ x 21½
From the Collection of the National Portrait Gallery

24. Edwin Booth in the title role of Shakespeare's *Hamlet*
by William Wallace Scott, 1870
Watercolor, 34¾ x 25
Lent by Harvard Theatre Collection

Edwin Booth's Prompt Book. In 1881 he appeared at London's Princess Theatre for a 119-night engagement and shortly after played at the Lyceum with Henry Irving, alternating with him the roles of Othello and Iago. From 1887 he played in this country principally with Lawrence Barrett and Helena Modjeska and in 1888 founded The Players in a house he had purchased on Gramercy Park in New York. His farewell from the stage was as Hamlet at the Brooklyn Academy of Music on 4 April 1891. It was a role he had made his own. All performances in America were henceforth to be judged by it. He died on 7 June 1893.

John McCullough
1832–1885

Born in the tiny village of Blakes, Ireland, on 14 November 1832, John McCullough was an illiterate youth when he came to Philadelphia in 1847. While teaching himself to read he discovered Shakespeare and soon joined an amateur theatrical group. After elocution lessons with Lemuel White, Edwin Forrest's teacher, he made his professional debut at the Arch Street Theatre on 15 August 1857. His first role was that of Thomas in *The Belle's Stratagem*. After spending the season 1860–1861 with Boston's Howard Athenaeum he was chosen by Edwin Forrest to be second actor in the American tragedian's company. In physique and stage manner he was much like Forrest and after five years of acting with him was criticized as being imitative. In 1866 McCullough left Forrest's company during a California tour and remained in San Francisco. In 1869 he was co-manager of that city's new California Theatre with Lawrence Barrett, and at the latter's withdrawal in 1870 he became sole manager and chief actor at that house for the next five years. McCullough began a series of national tours in 1873 and then returned to the East Coast for further acting lessons. New York critics who had once found fault with his unsubtle and boisterous acting now praised him. In the period from 1877 to 1883 he was at his peak as an actor of noble characters—Virginius, Brutus, Julius Ceasar, and Lear—and was favorably received. He was at his best in moments of rage, pathos, or passionate outbursts. He said he really experienced the emotions of the characters he was playing. Fellow actors often saw him shaking and weeping at the conclusion of a strong scene. About 1883 his health began to decline and he took a long vacation, returning to the stage in the autumn of 1884. During a performance of *The Gladiator* at McVicker's Theatre in Chicago on 29 September he suffered a mental and physical breakdown and had to be helped from the stage. From 27 June to 25 October of 1885 he was confined to a New York sanitarium. Taken home to Philadelphia, he died there on 8 November 1885.

25. John McCullough in the title role
of James Sheridan Knowles' *Virginius*
by Eastman Johnson, 1860
Oil on canvas, 36 x 30
Lent by The Players

Joseph Jefferson
1829-1905

Joseph Jefferson was the third of his name to appear on the American stage. His grandfather had immigrated from England in 1795, and his father was a traveling player and painter. Joseph was born in Philadelphia on 20 February 1829 and made his acting debut in Washington at age four with and as a miniature replica of the blackface comedian Thomas "Jim Crow" Rice. In 1837 he went with his family on a tour of the West and South. His father died during the tour and Joseph at age thirteen became the head of the family. In 1846, during the Mexican War, he even followed the United States Army across the border with the hopes of financial reward for his talents. By 1849 he had returned to New York where he joined the company at Chanfrau's National Theatre. In 1853 he was actor and stage manager in Baltimore, and in 1856 he made a trip to England and the Continent to observe the acting there as an aid to improving his own technique. Returning to New York he was engaged by Laura Keene at her theater and made his first big hit on 31 August 1857 when he acted Dr. Pangloss in George Colman's *The Heir-at-Law*. Upon the death of his wife in 1861 he left the United States and spent four years performing in Australia and Tasmania. In 1865 he returned to New York and left almost immediately for London where he and Dion Boucicault prepared a new stage version of Washington Irving's *Rip Van Winkle*. The greatness of his characterization of the title role was recognized immediately by the British public when he first performed the role at London's Adelphi Theatre on 4 September 1865, and when they saw him as Rip for the first time almost exactly a year later, on 3 September 1866, New Yorkers echoed the cheers of their cousins across the Atlantic. Joe Jefferson, as he was fondly called by his adoring American public, became a national institution as Rip Van Winkle. He toured the country annually in the role from 1866 on and put away the costumes for almost all of his characters, retaining only those for Dr. Pangloss and one or two others. He staged a revival of Richard Brinsley Sheridan's *The Rivals* with himself as Bob Acres at Philadelphia's Arch Street Theatre in 1880 and added this role to the select few he offered his public. Rip Van Winkle, of course, was his most popular role, and though he was proud and serious about his art he could laugh at himself and refer to the endless performances as "the theatrical swindle." In 1893, upon the death of Edwin Booth, The Players acknowledged his preeminence among American actors by electing him the second president of the organization. After seventy-one years on stage he last acted at Paterson, New Jersey, on 7 May 1904 as Caleb Plummer and Mr. Golightly in a double bill of *The Cricket on the Hearth* and *Lend Me Five Shillings*. He died at his home in Palm Beach, Florida, on 23 April 1905.

26. Joseph Jefferson as Peter Pangloss
in George Colman, Jr.'s *The Heir-in-Law*
by John Singer Sargent, 1891
Oil on canvas, 36 x 28½
Lent by The Players

27. Joseph Jefferson as Bob Acres
in Richard Brinsley Sheridan's *The Rivals*
by Robert F. Blum, 1881
Pencil on paper, approximately 11 x 5
Lent by Cincinnati Art Museum

Dion Boucicault
1822–1890

Remembered principally as a playwright, Dion Boucicault was born Dionysius Lardner Boursiquot in Dublin and began his association with the theater as an actor in provincial English playhouses under the name Lee Moreton. His first successful play, *London Assurance,* was produced in 1841. From 1844 until 1848 he was in France, where he met and married a French widow who mysteriously fell from a cliff while they were vacationing in the Alps. Dion Boucicault came to the United States for the first time in the fall of 1853. He had married the young actress Agnes Robertson in London and joined her in New York, where she made her debut in a musical that he had adapted from an older work. Agnes Robertson's success prompted an American tour during which her husband acted with her. Back in New York, Boucicault began to write and produce the long series of plays which kept him a favorite of American audiences during most of his stage career. *The Poor of New York* was a graphic if overly dramatic comment on the financial crisis of 1857, and *The Octoroon,* first produced in 1859, was so judiciously worded as to win the approbation of both slaveholders and abolitionists. In 1860 Boucicault produced *The Colleen Bawn,* the first of his comedies on an Irish theme. This play, a dramatization of Gerald Griffin's novel, *The Collegians,* was followed by three other plays in the same vein. Together these constitute the greatest monument to Dion Boucicault's abilities. *Arah-na-Pogue* appeared in 1864, *The O'Dowd* in 1873, and the following year the most famous of all, *The Shaughraun.* Boucicault excelled in Irish character roles and his own plays were his greatest vehicles. By the time of his appearances as Conn in *The Shaughraun* he had raised the stock comic character of the Irishman to the height of respectability. His popularity in the role prompted the New York sculptor John Rogers, whose interest in the theater was primarily commercial, to model Boucicault in character for production as a plaster parlor ornament. In the Spring of 1875 one of the completed statuettes was presented to Boucicault by Irish-American residents of New York as a testimonial of their appreciation for what his writing and acting had done to further the estate of the Irish in America. Boucicault returned to London from 1862 until 1872, and in 1885 he went to Australia for a short time. His major achievements, however, remained connected with the history of the New York stage. In addition to his writing and acting he had also instituted the practice of casting a play in New York and sending a complete production on tour. It was a practice that had serious effects on the older tradition of local stock companies. Dion Boucicault appeared on stage for the last time in 1886. Having spent his fortunes almost before he acquired them, he had sunk to the relatively insignificant position of a teacher of acting at the time of his death in New York on 18 September 1890.

28. Dion Boucicault as Conn with his dog Tatters
in Boucicault's *The Shaughraun*
by John Rogers, 1874–1875
Bronze, 20 inches high (master model for the plasters)
Lent by The New-York Historical Society

THE SHAUGHRAUN AND "TATTERS"

Adelina Patti
1843-1919

Born in Madrid of Italian parents, Adelina Patti was brought to New York at a very early age, and it was there that she made her debut as a concert singer when but seven years old. Coached by her brother-in-law Maurice Strakosch she sang under his direction locally and on a tour of New Orleans and the West Indies in a group that included the pianist Louis Moreau Gottschalk. On 24 November 1859 she made her operatic debut in the title role of Gaetano Donizetti's *Lucia di Lammermoor* at New York's Academy of Music. From that moment on it was clear to everyone including Adelina that she was destined to be a prima donna. By the time she made her European debut at the Royal Italian Opera of London on 14 May 1861 as Amina in Bellini's *La Sonnambula,* she was hailed as the successor to Giulia Grisi and Jenny Lind and as such reigned as a true diva for forty-five years. She had a pure tone and an impeccable technique, having been schooled in the virtuoso bel canto style that may be said to have retired from the stage when she did. Even though some of her contemporaries made fun of her manner-isms—she never overtaxed herself, vocally or emotionally; she walked to the footlights for all her solo arias, ignoring whatever else might be happening on the stage; and she had cushions provided for her death scenes so that she might die in comfort—they all acknowledged that she was indeed a "Queen of Song." Critics such as New York's Henry T. Finck castigated her for the mediocrity of much of the music she sang, charging that she was interested only in showing off her lovely voice. Even he, however, later capitulated to her vocal artistry and called hers, "the sweetest and most mellow voice the world has ever heard." She had an incomparable way of "milking" applause from her audiences, both in individual performances and throughout her career. Time and again she would disappear behind the curtain at the end of a performance only to reappear with more bows and fresh blown kisses if the applause showed signs of dying away too soon. As early as the spring of 1887, while singing at the Metropolitan Opera House with a visiting touring company, she allowed impresario Henry E. Abbey to spread the word that this engagement would be her "farewell to opera." Only the most indefatigable student of opera can catalogue her "farewells." There was another at the Met again in April 1890, and in November of 1903 she sang her first concert in yet another tour billed as her "last." By now her voice had lost much of its bloom but was still masterfully handled. One New York critic, however, was so subtly unkind as to write, "It is unfortunate that the great artist has not been willing to leave us with mem-ories of achievements which were, in their own particular way, worthy to be put with the supreme tradition of art . . ." Her last appearance onstage was on 20 October 1914 at a benefit concert for the Red Cross in the Albert Hall of London. The last thing she ever sang was "Home, Sweet Home," the song which had been a favorite encore and her trademark throughout her career. She was seventy-two and she had been onstage for over fifty-six years. After a short illness, she died on 27 September 1919 at Craig-y-Nos, her castle home in Brecknock, Wales.

29. Adelina Patti
by James Sant, circa 1886
Oil on canvas, 43 ½ x 33 ½

Lent by National Portrait Gallery, London

Sarah Bernhardt was born in Paris on 23 October 1844. The daughter of a courtisan, she was an actress from that moment in her childhood when she realized she could hold an audience. Encouraged by two of her mother's more influential friends, Alexandre Dumas père and the Duc de Morny, she auditioned and won admission to the dramatic school of the Paris Conservatoire. She made her debut with the Comédie Française in the title role of Jean Racine's *Iphigénie* in 1862 and within a year was dismissed for slapping one of the older actresses. It was the first of many offstage incidents which kept her in the public eye. She went on to play in other Parisian theaters, notably the Odéon, where she had her first taste of stardom in 1868. By 1872 she was the most talked about actress in France, both for her performances onstage and her eccentric behavior off. In the same year she was reengaged by the Comédie. With that company in 1874 she played for the first time the title role in Racine's *Phèdre,* a role considered one of her greatest artistic achievements throughout her long career. In 1880 she played Marguerite Gauthier in Alexandre Dumas fils' play *La Dame aux Camélias* for the first time. Billed as *Camille* it was a play that was ever popular with her American audiences. She made nine tours of the United States, the first beginning at Booth's Theatre in New York on 8 November 1880 with Sarah, or "The Bernhardt" as her American fans called her, in the title role of Eugène Scribe's *Adrienne Lecouvreur.* From New York she went on tour in a palatial railroad car and acted 157 performances in fifty-one cities. Sixty-five of these performances were as Marguerite Gauthier. If money is a measure of success, the $194,000 in gold she took back to France with her at the end of the tour tell more than any press reviews. She was a great actress and an eccentric, unpredictable, incandescent personality. She held her audiences spellbound with technique and with a voice which a critic in the *New York Times,* writing at the beginning of her second American tour in March of 1887, described as "strangely sweet in moods of tenderness and thrilling in bursts of passion." In 1882 she had created the title role of the vengeful Russian princess in Victorien Sardou's *Fédora,* and from then on her repertoire always included sumptuously staged productions of the plays that master of melodrama created for her. American and European audiences both were thrilled by her characterizations of Sardou's heroines Théodora, Floria Tosca, Cléopâtre, and Gismonda. Sarah Bernhardt was above all else a great show woman, and so it is not surprising that her last four tours of the United States between 1905 and 1918 were each billed as a "Farewell Tour." During the first of these emotional and lucrative peregrinations she ran up against the opposition of the powerful New York Theatrical Syndicate and was forced to play in rollerskating rinks, and at one point, while in Texas, in a tent. She was without a doubt one of the greatest theatrical personalities of her time, if not the greatest actress. There were those who considered her the principal ambassador of her native country, and France accordingly made her a Chevalier of the Légion d'Honneur in March of 1914. Eleven months later she had a leg amputated as the result of an old knee injury. Undaunted, however, she returned to the stage in the autumn of 1915 without benefit of crutches or artificial leg.

30. Sarah Bernhardt in the title role of Victorien Sardou's *Fédora*
by Alfred Stevens, 1882
Oil on canvas, 53 x 45½

Lent by Peter A. Salm

She acted most of her roles sitting. She became so important that during World War I she was listed as one of the hostages desired in Germany upon the capture of Paris. She counteracted this threat by acting for the French troops at the front lines. In 1916 she came to the United States for what was to be her real farewell tour. Between professional engagements she devoted much of her time to raising funds for European war casualties and being a rabble rouser for the Allied cause. She returned to France just as the Armistice was being signed. Although her health was declining she worked practically until the time of her death. She created four new roles in the last three years of her life and was working on a motion picture in her home up until five days before her death. She died in Paris on 26 March 1923 and was buried in the cemetery of Père Lachaise beneath her epitaph that reads simply and eloquently "Bernhardt."

Born John Henry Brodribb, it was as Henry Irving that he made his first appearance on the English stage in September of 1856. In the next twenty years he appeared throughout the British Isles and by August 1878 had acquired his own company and the management of the Lyceum Theatre in London, which he held until 1902. With himself in the title role and Ellen Terry as his Ophelia, he opened the theater on 30 December 1878 with a production of Shakespeare's *Hamlet*. Immediately the critics took notice of Irving's insistence on tasteful costumes and scenery and perfection of ensemble. At the Lyceum, early in 1881, Henry Irving began his first association with the American theater by acting with the visiting Edwin Booth. Only moderately successful from the Briton's point of view, during his run at the Princess Theatre, Booth was invited to alternate the title role and that of Iago with Irving in a production of Shakespeare's *Othello*. On Monday, Wednesday, and Friday of the first week Booth appeared as Othello and Irving as Iago; the following week they reversed roles. The engagement began on 2 May 1881 and lasted for twenty-two performances; Ellen Terry was the Desdemona to both the British and American Othellos. In the autumn of 1883 Henry Irving took his company of nearly half a hundred actors and tons of scenery and costumes on its first tour of America. It was the first of eight tours which he was to make of the United States between 1883 and 1904. They lasted four to eight months each, and as in the case of the second tour took Irving and Ellen Terry, who was his leading lady on all but the last tour, into Canada as well. All the tours were immensely successful, both critically and financially. It is said that within one month of the beginning of the first tour, Irving and company had taken in a quarter of a million dollars at the box office. Henry Irving's sumptuous productions and intelligent staging were without doubt the finest theater to be seen in America in their time. Shakespeare's works were, of course, always the staple of repertory, but the plays of other playwrights were not neglected. On his third tour, Irving's spectacular production of *Faust* was the principal work, and during the fourth tour from September of 1893 to March 1894, Alfred Lord Tennyson's *Becket* was played most often. During his fifth tour, which lasted from September 1895 until May of 1896, Comyn Carr's *King Arthur,* with scenery by Edward Burne-Jones and incidental music by Sir Arthur Sullivan, was the principal offering to American audiences. In 1895 he was knighted by Queen Victoria for his services to the stage, the first British actor to be so honored. His last tour of America ended in March of 1904, and he acted for the last time at Bradford, England, on 13 October 1905 in the title role of *Becket*. Returning to his hotel after the performance, he collapsed and died almost immediately. One week later his ashes were interred in Westminster Abbey.

31. Sir Henry Irving in the title role of Shakespeare's *Richard III*
by Edwin Long, 1877
Oil on canvas, 61½ x 43½
Lent by American Shakespeare Festival Theatre

Anton Seidl
1850-1898

There were many who supposed that Anton Seidl was the son of Franz Liszt. If that is so, he followed well his illustrious father's artistic footsteps. At age twenty-two Seidl was engaged by Richard Wagner to aid the "Meister" of music drama in his work at Bayreuth. He assisted in the completion of the scores of the *Ring* cycle and of *Parsifal* and handled many of the performance details of the first festival at Bayreuth in 1876. In 1879 he became a conductor at the Leipzig Opera, and in the season of 1882–1883 he traveled throughout Europe spreading the gospel of Wagner's new music. In 1884 he was appointed conductor at the Bremen Opera. On 23 November 1885 he made his debut at the Metropolitan Opera House which had hired him to replace the recently deceased Leopold Damrosch. Opera at the Met from the years of 1885 to 1890 was offered exclusively in German for social and economic reasons, so Seidl introduced the operas of Wagner whenever he could. New York heard *Die Meistersinger* for the first time on 4 January 1886. *Rienzi* received its first hearing a month later. *Tristan und Isolde* premiered on 1 December 1886, and *Siegfried* and *Götterdämmerung* appeared in the season of 1887–1888. In 1891 the backers of the Metropolitan had had enough of opera in German and demoted it in favor of the musical products of southern and western Europe. Anton Seidl left the Metropolitan and became the conductor of the Philharmonic Society of New York. In 1893 he conducted that orchestra at the major non-Wagnerian event of his career in this country—the American premiere of his friend Anton Dvorak's *New World Symphony*. In the seasons of 1895–1896 and 1896–1897 he returned to the Metropolitan to conduct the great Polish tenor Jean de Reszke in notable revivals of Wagner. Realizing the great talent he had brought to their city, a group of New York music lovers was attempting to create and endow a permanent orchestra for Seidl when he died of ptomaine poisoning on 28 March 1898. His funeral was held on 31 March 1898 in the Metropolitan Opera House, the scene of his greatest American triumphs.

32. Anton Seidl
by Frank Eugene, 1894
Oil on canvas, 50 x 34
Lent by The New-York Historical Society

Carmencita (Carmen Dauset)
1868 or 1869

Carmencita was one of the first "ethnic" dancers to appear in the United States. She was not an immediate success when she first appeared at Niblo's Garden in New York, but in the spring of 1890, while dancing nightly at Koster and Bial's Music Hall, she became one of the most popular theatrical attractions in the city. Readers of the theatrical columns were told that she lived on Amontillado sherry and fruit and were treated to speculation that she had heart disease and to delightfully frank descriptions of their heroine at home. Front-page news to the contrary, she had a sound heart, but she was a disappointment to those who saw her in her unguarded moments offstage. She danced nightly at the music halls, tutored matinee dancing classes in Madison Avenue Mansions, and appeared in private concerts for select groups in artists' studios. The thought of seeing the exotic Spanish dancer in so terribly chic and romantic an atmosphere so enthused Isabella Stewart Gardner that she made a special trip from Boston to be one of the audience at a command performance in the studio of William Merritt Chase. The co-host was John Singer Sargent. At the end of a particularly rousing dance, delighted guests threw flowers and jewelry. One of the ladies reflected upon her overemotional response and the next day asked that her trinket be returned. Carmencita, bless her heart, refused. The true measure of Carmencita's success in America was in the number of imitators who came after her. Because she was first, or because she was good, they never quite measured up.

33. Carmencita
by William Merritt Chase, 1890
Oil on canvas, 70 x 40⅛
Lent by Metropolitan Museum of Art, Gift of Sir William Van Horne, 1906

The son of a German opera-singer mother and an English wine-merchant father, Richard Mansfield was born in Germany on 24 May 1854 and came to America with his mother in 1872. In Boston where they settled he joined an amateur theatrics group and appeared on stage for the first time early in 1876. He wanted to be a painter and returned to London in 1877 where he soon learned that his chosen profession would not be lucrative. He began giving entertainments in private homes and music halls and toured for a while as Sir Joseph Porter in Gilbert and Sullivan's operetta *H.M.S. Pinafore*. He returned to the United States in April of 1882 and made his first really professional appearance on an American stage at New York's Standard Theatre as Dromez in the operetta *Les Manteaux Noirs* on 27 September. He played stock and operetta for three years and in September of 1885, after a very short return trip to London, he was again in New York supporting Minnie Maddern in *In Spite of All*. His first real success was in the title role of Archibald C. Gunter's *Prince Karl,* which he first acted in Boston on 5 April 1886. From there the play went to New York and on tour for exactly one year. On 9 May 1887 he performed for the first time in the dual roles of Dr. Jekyll and Mr. Hyde in the play by Thomas Russell Sullivan. Throughout his career his audiences were never to tire of watching his evidently spectacular onstage transformation from one character to another. In August of 1888 he took the play to London and while there acted Shakespeare for the first time. The role was Richard III and it was to remain one of his most popular. On 19 May 1890 at New York's Madison Square Theatre he added Clyde Fitch's *Beau Brummel* to his growing repertoire, and in 1893 he acted Shylock for the first time. On 17 September 1894 he produced *Arms and the Man* at the Herald Square Theatre. It was the first production of a George Bernard Shaw play that America had seen, and although it was not exactly an overwhelming success—it lasted sixteen performances—Mansfield chose it to open his management of the Garrick Theatre in April of 1895. He also produced the second Shaw play in America—*The Devil's Disciple* —which opened in Albany on 1 October 1897. From 1900 to 1906 he produced and acted in a repertoire that included not only his favored characterizations, but Shakespeare's *Henry V* and *Julius Caesar,* Booth Tarkington's *Monsieur Beaucaire,* and the first performance in this country of Henrik Ibsen's *Peer Gynt*. His style was highly individual, and he was as committed to scrupulous preparation of a production as was his contemporary Mrs. Fiske, but sadly lacked her offstage personality and her consideration for subordinates. His outbursts of temperament were legend in his profession long before his death. He fell ill after acting a double bill in New York on 23 March 1907 and died at his home in New London, Connecticut, on 23 August of that year. When he died there were those who saw the passing of an era, an era of the "grand style" and of repertory theater.

34. Richard Mansfield in the title role of Clyde Fitch's *Beau Brummel*
by Orlando Rouland, 1907
Oil on canvas, 83¼ x 40
From the collection of the National Portrait Gallery

Minnie Maddern Fiske
1865-1932

The daughter of theatrical parents, Maria August Davey was born in New Orleans on 19 December 1865. She is said to have made her stage debut in Little Rock, Arkansas, at the age of three using the name, "Little Minnie Maddern." She was seen in New York for the first time in 1870 in two different roles, one of them Little Eva in *Uncle Tom's Cabin*. By the time she made her real professional debut at the Park Theatre in May of 1882, she had had experience in a wide range of theatrics. In 1884 she was very successful in a musical called *Caprice*. On 19 May 1890 she married Harrison Grey Fiske, editor of the *New York Dramatic Mirror* and briefly retired from the stage. She returned again in 1894 as the tragedienne Mrs. Fiske in the title role of her husband's *Hester Crewe*. Both playwright and actress attempted with this work to break away from the traditions of the nineteenth century. After long years of practice and experience she evolved a personal style which made her a pioneer on the American stage. She emphasized a truthfulness and true-to-life portrayal of her characters, and she strove for a production in which the performers and stage effects were all subordinate to the overall aim of the author. It would be years before the rest of her profession and the public caught up with her ideals. She knew that all in life was not the proverbial sweetness and light, and she achieved great success in her portrayals of immoral and unsavory women in Lorrimer Stoddard's *Tess of the D'Ubervilles* in 1897 and Langdon Mitchell's *Becky Sharp* in 1899. Most of her history-making productions were staged between 1901 and 1907 at the Manhattan Theatre, which her husband had bought for her when the Klaw and Erlanger Syndicate evicted her from the Fifth Avenue Theatre at the height of her success in *Becky Sharp*. A champion of Henrik Ibsen in a day when American critics and playgoers thought him immoral and subversive, she first played Nora in his *A Doll's House* at a benefit in 1894 and produced *Hedda Gabler* and *Rosmersholm* at her own theater in 1903 and 1907. Against the fulminations of critics and clergymen alike she played the latter Ibsen work for an unprecedented 199 performances at a profit. She acted Mrs. Alving in her fifth Ibsen production, *Ghosts,* which toured the country in 1927. During the latter part of her career she acted mainly in lighter comedy, and one of her last roles was as Beatrice in *Much Ado about Nothing,* the first Shakespeare she had played since her childhood. She declared acting to be a science and she devoted her whole life to it. Outside of the theater her only interests were the prevention of cruelty to animals and the wanton slaying of animals and birds for fur and feathers. During the last years she revived some of her earlier successes and took them on the road. Illness forced her to cancel her tour early in 1932 and she died at her Hollis, Long Island, home on 15 February of that year.

35. Minnie Maddern Fiske
by M. Colin, 1893
Oil on canvas, 71⅞ x 48¼
From the collection of the National Portrait Gallery

[80]

Loie Fuller
1862-1928

It's a long way from Fullersburg, Illinois, to Paris, France. Loie Fuller made the trip with a certain verve that would be hard to exceed. At age four she made her debut with a stock company in Chicago. Impersonations of little boys became her specialty. She toured with Buffalo Bill's Wild West Company and sang at least one performance of grand opera at Hooley's Opera House in Chicago. Both vaudeville and legitimate theater stages exposed her talent to public view. After a short run in London in a trifle entitled *Caprice* she returned to New York where, in 1891, she evolved the "Serpentine Dance" which was to bring her fame in both Europe and America. As she danced she manipulated the folds of a long skirt about her in constantly changing billows. She became enamored with light and by the time she had reached Paris in 1892—by way of short engagements with a German theater and a French traveling circus—she had conceived such innovations in the lighting of her act that she was signed by the Folies Bergère. She considered herself an instrument of light and invented and named dances that were inspired by colors and by sensations of light. In her *"Fire Dance"* she performed on a sheet of glass lighted from below in an effort to capture the effects of flame and smoke. It was this dance that inspired the Toulouse-Lautrec lithograph. Loie Fuller's dancing was everything that the lovers of the then blossoming Art Nouveau style wanted from a work of art. It had color, sinuous line, and real movement. Instantly, she was the idol of Paris. In 1896 she returned to New York for a short engagement at Koster and Bial's Music Hall and enthralled that city's audiences as she had those in the French capital. Her weekly salary was reputed to be twice that of the ever-popular Lillian Russell. She picnicked with Auguste Rodin, was introduced to the French Astronomical Society by Camille Flammarion, the celebrated astronomer, was depicted on posters by Jules Cheret and other leading artists of the genre, and she became the inspiration for a bronze lamp by Raoul Larche. In short, she became one of the major motifs of Art Nouveau. Her studies of light became quite serious, and she constantly improved and elaborated upon her stage effects. One of her dances, the *"Fire Dance"* already mentioned, required the services of fourteen electricians. She became a friend of Pierre and Marie Curie, whose discovery of radium seemed to Loie the source of a very special lighting effect she might use in her act. In her constant search for more impressive lighting effects she maintained a laboratory with sometimes as many as six employees working on experiments with "fluorescent salts." She once seared some of her hair and was evicted from her quarters when an experiment she was conducting blew up in her face. A troupe which she gathered about her and which she presented in concert included for a while the young Isadora Duncan. Her band of comely young "muses," as she called them, appeared with her in a "Ballet of Light." During the First World War she traveled back and forth between France and America arranging entertainments for servicemen and campaigning for wartime charities. As early as 1905 she made motion pictures in the Paris studios of the Pathé company. Her last professional performance in 1927 was in a

36. Loie Fuller dancing her *"Fire Dance"*
by Henry de Toulouse-Lautrec, 1893
Lithograph, 14⁷⁄₁₆ x 10⅛
Lent by National Gallery of Art, Rosenwald Collection

[82]

"Shadow Ballet" which utilized silhouette effects suggested to her by the developments in cinema technique. In her never ending efforts to create new stage lighting lies her great contribution to stagecraft. Her contributions to choreography, if there were any, have paled aside her capability to create an effect. She summed up her position herself when she said, "I suppose I am the only person who is known as a dancer but who has a personal preference for Science."

Eleonora Duse
1859-1924

She was the daughter of traveling players and she had played Juliet in Verona at age four-teen. European theatergoers had praised her acting for years, but when she first appeared in New York in 1893 Eleonora Duse was not well known to American audiences. After her first performance as Marguerite in Dumas' *La Dame aux Camelias,* she was praised as highly in the New World as she was in the Old. She performed only in Italian, which was a handicap, and although some of the New York critics found her no improvement over the "Divine Sarah," they all had to admit to the stunning power of the naturalism of her acting. A commentator in *Harper's Weekly* for 18 March 1893 said, "in seeing Miss Duse we lose sight entirely of the woman in the artist, and are only conscious of a per-sonality so absorbing and so magnetic that it can sway our emotion at will. . . ." She returned to the United States in 1896 and in 1902, bringing with her on her third tour only the plays of Gabriele D'Annunzio whose characters, some created for her, were of a pathetic nature well suited to Duse's own character. One perceptive critic wrote, "She seems to live her character; tears from her come on as a natural consequence." Her artistry was applauded, but American audiences found the D'Annunzio plays gruesome and distasteful. As her health failed, Duse announced her retirement from the stage in 1909. Financial losses during World War I forced her to come out of retirement in 1921, and she began her farewell tour of the United States at the Metropolitan Opera House in October of 1923. John Corbin, writing of her opening night performance in Henrik Ibsen's *The Lady from the Sea,* unwittingly penned a review that read like an epitaph, "Many were present last night who welcomed Duse thirty years ago, when she ran the whole gamut from stark tragedy to comedy airily light. In that generation no voice has been heard even faintly resembling hers—nor is such a voice ever likely to be heard again." She was last seen on stage at the Syria Mosque in Pittsburgh on 5 April 1924. She caught a cold which developed into influenza and pneumonia and died in her room at the Hotel Schenley on 21 April 1924.

37. Eleonora Duse
by Auguste Rodin, before 1917
Bronze, 9⅛ inches high
Lent by Worcester Art Museum

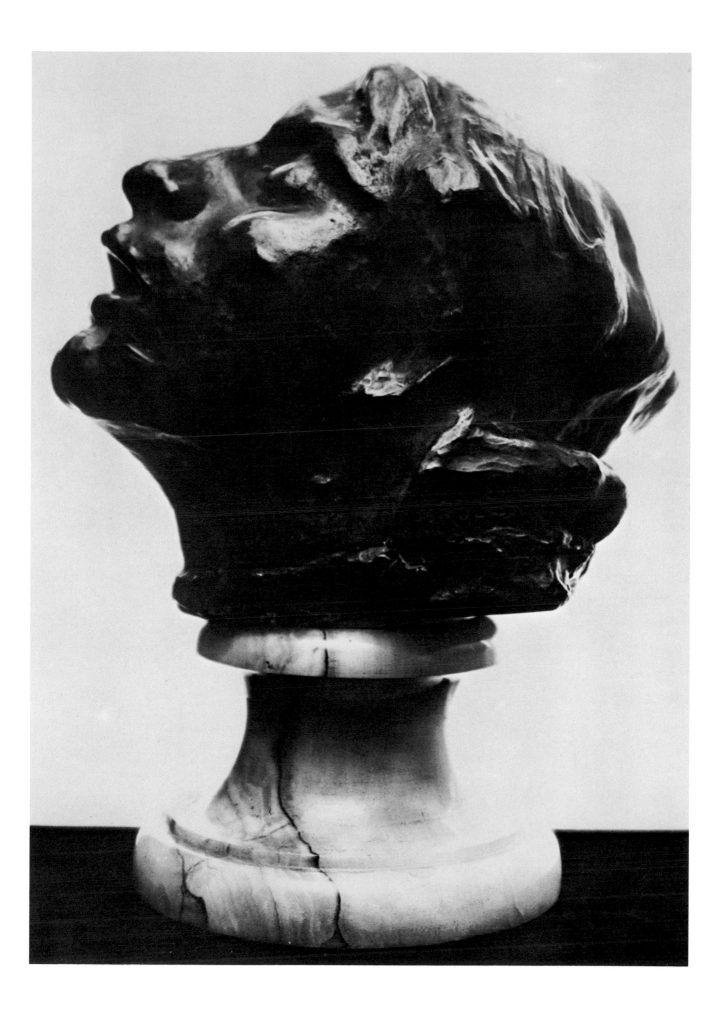

Emma Calvé
1853-1942

Sophisticates that they were, New York opera audiences in 1893 accepted Wagnerian Amazons in cowhorns and bearskins, but they expected the female singers in the Italian and French operas to look and act like ladies. More than a few eyebrows were raised on the evening of 29 November when Emma Calvé made her Metropolitan Opera debut singing the role of Santuzza in Leoncavallo's *Cavalleria Rusticana*. Wearing actual Italian peasant clothes and acting with a rudeness suited to the character, she brought New York its first real taste of the new brand of *verismo* lyric drama. Critics admired Calvé's performances—vocal and dramatic—but the opera did not find favor with the public. As a substitute, Bizet's *Carmen* was billed, and thus on 10 December 1893 the New World saw and heard Emma Calvé for the first time in the role that she had made her own. When she was three months old her family left their native France and went to live in Spain. There they remained until Emma was seven. She therefore knew of gypsies firsthand. She had listened to their songs. She had danced their dances. She was not about to let an opera-house manager tell her that her Carmen should be a lady. Reviewing her first Metropolitan performance in the role, W. J. Henderson in the *New York Times* said, "Her Carmen is a creature of unbridled passion, graceful with a sensuous, suggestive grace, and careless of all consequences." He also noted that "in the second act her impersonation approached the boundary of the hazardous." Emma herself agreed later that she did sometimes get carried away. But then, that's how gypsies are. It was not her favorite role, but until the advent of Geraldine Farrar, it was the role American audiences wanted her to sing. During the Manhattan Opera House season of 1906–1907 popular demand fostered nineteen performances of the work. After leaving the operatic stage Emma retired to a castle in southern France. Some of her time was spent with a select handful of pupils. Some of it was filled, assuredly, with satisfied memories of what she herself certainly considered the most outstanding moment of her American career—a night in June 1916 when she knelt before an audience of ten thousand in a New York armory, sang the "Marseillaise" with tears streaming down her cheeks, and collected one hundred thousand dollars for French war relief.

38. Emma Calvé in the title role of Georges Bizet's *Carmen*
by Théobald Chartran, 1894
Oil on canvas, 45$\frac{11}{16}$ x 35$\frac{1}{2}$
Lent by Sterling and Francine Clark Art Institute

After a short career as a child actress on the West Coast, Maude Adams came to New York and made her first professional appearance in that city in September of 1888. She acted with E. H. Sothern and was leading lady to John Drew for five years before becoming a star in her own right. On 27 September 1897 she appeared at the Empire Theatre for the first time as Lady Babbie in James Barrie's *The Little Minister*. An unidentified reviewer has left us an honest and engaging description of her appearance in her first starring role, "Miss Adams is a fascinating gypsy, with queer little gestures and an odd tiptoe walk that is like no gait ever affected by a sane human creature, but somehow seems to fit the part . . . Her speech is eerie—but not too eerie." Sensing that she would color all her characters with her own personality, the critic Alan Dale wrote shortly after her opening, "Any role that is bijou, archly feminine, girlishly effervescent and plaintive will suit this elf-actress. Let her avoid the Juliets and the Rosalinds and the Fedoras and the Camilles. Let her listen to those who know better than she does, and Miss Adams will remain with us, and her art will grow even more subtle." Either he was a prophet or Miss Adams listened to advice. She avoided all roles that did not feature youthful, good, and optimistic characters, and she excelled in the realm of the sweetly sentimental. On 6 November 1905 she opened again at the Empire and again in a play by Barrie. It was *Peter Pan*—the most favored and memorable role for both the actress and her enchanted audiences. Miss Adams valued her privacy, and even though she became wealthy and famous as the greatest box-office attraction of her time she never gave press interviews. Even so, the press was kind and most of what appeared about her in magazines and newspapers extolled her humility and homeness. In 1918 she retired from the stage and spent some time experimenting with stage lighting. She returned to acting in 1931 playing Portia to Otis Skinner's Shylock in an ill-fated production of *The Merchant of Venice* that never made it to Broadway; she toured summer theaters in a small part in *Twelfth Night* in 1934. In 1937 she joined the faculty of Stephens College, Columbia, Missouri, as a professor of dramatic arts. She died at Tannersville, New York, on 17 July 1953.

39. Maude Adams as Lady Babbie in James Barrie's *The Little Minister*
by Howard Chandler Christy, 1899
Pastel on paper, 39¾ x 20½
Lent by Stephens College

Julia Marlowe
1865–1950

She was born in Caldbeck, England, on 17 August 1865 as Sarah Frances Frost and at age five she was brought to the United States and raised in Cincinnati. As a child actress she first appeared on stage billed as Fanny Brough. The name by which she became famous, Julia Marlowe, was chosen by combining the name of the character she played in Knowle's *The Hunchback* with the last name of Christopher Marlowe. Her childhood knowledge of Shakespeare prompted a neighbor, Ada Dow, to take her to New York and groom her for a theatrical career. In 1887 teacher Dow engaged a company of players to surround her fledgling star and sent all of them on a New England tour with W. S. Gilbert's *Pygmalion and Galatea*. In October the Bijou Theatre was hired for a matinee performance of *Ingomar* starring Julia Marlowe in her New York debut. Those who attended seem to have been impressed by the capabilities of the eighteen-year-old actress. She was eventually engaged to play Shakespearian roles at the Star Theatre where she married her leading man, Robert Taber, in 1894. Six years later they were divorced. Her success in the dramatization of Charles Major's novel *When Knighthood Was in Flower* made her independently wealthy. In 1904 she acted for the first time with E. H. Sothern in a notable production of *Hamlet*. They were married in 1911. Passionately devoted to Shakespeare—in a slightly perverse manner that prompted them to cut all passages they thought bawdy—they were, however, conscientious in their endeavors and their productions were never dull. The *Macbeth* they produced and acted in 1910 is thought to be their finest joint achievement. Julia Marlowe's Lady Macbeth was not only a characterization original for its time, but her undoubted masterpiece. She and Sothern both began to retire in 1915 and left the stage in 1924. In 1926 they ended their career in the theater by staging ten of Shakespeare's plays for the Memorial Theater in Stratford-on-Avon. In 1929 in remembrance of things past Julia Marlowe was awarded a gold medal by the American Academy of Arts and Letters. After her husband's death in 1933 she went into seclusion and died in her rooms in New York's Plaza Hotel on 12 November 1950.

40. Julia Marlowe
by Irving R. Wiles, 1901
Oil on canvas, 74 x 55¼
Lent by National Gallery of Art

Ethel Barrymore
1879-1959

She really wanted to be a concert pianist, but born of a great theatrical family, Ethel Barrymore went on the stage instead. She made her stage debut in a bit part in *The Rivals,* and her apprenticeship included minor roles with her uncle, John Drew, in New York and with Sir Henry Irving's company in London. Although the critics in her hometown of Philadelphia were anything but kind when she opened there as Madame Trentoni in Clyde Fitch's *Captain Jinks of the Horse Marines,* Ethel Barrymore became a star when the play arrived at the Garrick Theatre in New York on 4 February 1901. Four weeks later her name was up in lights and stayed there throughout her long career. Her audiences adored her in light comedy and were disturbed when she attempted to break out of the stereotype roles in which they revered her. They were perturbed in 1907 when she appeared as a scrubwoman in John Galsworthy's *The Silver Box,* although some of the professional critics were impressed, and in 1910 her acting of Zoë Blundell in Sir Arthur Pinero's *Midchannel* was only begrudgingly accepted as passable. Her own tastes in the drama on the whole were rather conservative; she was not receptive to the more advanced playwrights. In 1905 she did appear in a production of Henrik Ibsen's *A Doll's House* with her brother John, but she found the Norwegian's characters perverted and false and she dismissed George Bernard Shaw's plays as trivial. Her professional reputation was notably enhanced by her performance in Barrie's *Alice-Sit-by-the-Fire* in 1905, when she played a motherly role for the first time, and by her appearances in Somerset Maugham's *Lady Frederick* in 1908. Her critics and fans were especially happy when she returned to a lighter comedy part in Edna Ferber and G. V. Hobart's *Our Mrs. McChesney* in 1915. In 1919 she opened as Lady Helen Haden in Zoë Akins' *Déclassée,* a role particularly well suited to her talents. Regally confident of her abilities she saw nothing wrong with playing Juliet when she was forty-three and Ophelia and Portia when she was forty-six. Her playing of Lady Teazle in The Players' 1925 production of *School for Scandal* became one of the more brilliant facets of her career, and in 1925 she was also well received for her acting in Somerset Maugham's *The Constant Wife.* Ethel Barrymore was the undisputed "First Lady of the American Stage" in 1928 and the Schuberts named a new theater in her honor, which she inaugurated on 20 December by opening as Sister Garcia in Martinez Sierra's *The Kingdom of God.* Her motion picture debut, in the only film she ever made with both brothers John and Lionel, occurred in 1933 in *Rasputin and the Empress.* In 1940 she almost refused the role of the Welsh schoolteacher Miss Moffat in Emlyn Williams' *The Corn is Green* as being unsuited for her. She played it, however, and it proved to be perhaps the finest performance of her career. As her health failed she spent more and more time in California. In 1950 she returned to Broadway to act in a benefit performance for the American National Theater and Academy. At the fall of the curtain a grand ovation forced her to take several curtain calls. Acknowledging the applause she said, "You make it sound inviting." These were her last words on the Broadway stage. She returned to Hollywood, where she died 18 June 1959.

41. Ethel Barrymore as Madame Trentoni in Clyde Fitch's
Captain Jinks of the Horse Marines
by Sigismund de Ivanowski, 1901?
Oil on canvas, 68 x 50
Lent by Museum of the City of New York, Theatre and Music Collection

Enrico Caruso
1873-1921

For thousands, though they may never even have heard his voice on records, the name of the tenor Enrico Caruso evokes the grandness of opera. His career in this country was almost exclusively associated with the Metropolitan Opera. From a short time after his debut there as the Duke of Mantua in Verdi's *Rigoletto* on 23 November 1903 until his 607th performance—and his last—at that house on 24 December 1920 as Eleazer in Jacques Halévy's *La Juive,* he was one of the most important singers on the company roster. With his powerful voice, and bolstered by the enthusiasm of the growing Italian population of New York, he effected a pronounced change upon the repertory which up until that time had been top-heavy with Germanic works. Verdi's *Aida* and Leoncavallo's *I Pagliacci* became, because of his presence in lead roles, audience favorites. Under the baton of Arturo Toscanini from 1908 until 1915 he aided the establishment of the operas of Puccini. In that composer's *La Fanciulla del West,* based on a David Belasco play, he created the role of Dick Johnson at the opera's Metropolitan Opera world premiere on 10 December 1910. Shortly after his New York debut he made his first recording for RCA Victor. In an era when some of his fellow singers mistrusted the respectability of the phonograph and recorded under aliases, his open endorsement helped greatly to promote the infant industry. His last recordings made three months before his final stage performance include that which he himself considered his finest. Ironically, it is the aria "Rachel, quand du Seigneur" from that last opera, *La Juive.* Caruso had the unprecedented honor of being part of the opening night cast sixteen out of his seventeen years with the Metropolitan Opera. A most honest critic of his own performances, the endorsement of his paycheck stubs often included a one word appraisal of that evening's performance. They range from "Not so good" to "Magnificent." In ill health from pleurisy he left the stage at the end of 1920 and returned to his native Italy. He died at Naples, 9:05 a.m. on the morning of 2 August 1921. The following day W. J. Henderson in the New York *Sun* printed the news of his death. Part of that column was an accurate and eloquent eulogy:

In sincerity, in fervor, in devotion to his art, he was the peer of any opera singer in history. . . . He was an indifferent actor and a supreme singer when he came here. He finished his career a singer less flawless, but an operatic interpreter who commanded the respect and sympathy of the severest critics, even when they could not credit him with a triumphant success.

42. Enrico Caruso
by Filippo Cifariello, 1910
Silver, 29 inches high
Lent by Metropolitan Opera Association

Geraldine Farrar
1882-1967

Born in Melrose, Massachusetts, 28 February 1882, Geraldine Farrar went to Europe to taste her first stage success. She made her debut with the Berlin Opera on 15 October 1901. Her voice and beauty made her an immediate favorite. Much to the chagrin of the director of the Opera, Miss Farrar's special patronage by the royal family granted her a dispensation to sing her roles in Italian while the rest of the company sang in the usual German. Her debut at the Metropolitan Opera House on 26 November 1906, at age twenty-four, as the heroine in the Charles Gounod setting of Shakespeare's *Romeo and Juliet,* was highly anticipated by critics and public alike. Henry Krehbiel's review in the *New York Tribune* preechoed the public attitude which was to persist throughout her Met career, ". . . she achieved a place among those whom a Metropolitan audience recognizes as in the forefront of the world's operatic artists." For almost twenty years Geraldine Farrar and Enrico Caruso reigned jointly as the most profitable and popular singers on the Metropolitan roster. Her voice was admired, but critics went into raptures over her acting of Carmen, the Goose Girl, in Engelbert Humperdinck's *Königskinder*—she insisted on having live geese—and of the title role in Ruggerio Leoncavallo's *Zaza.* At her first performance of the latter role, 16 January 1920, her loyal following of young girl fans, called "gerryflappers" by the press, went into hysterics, and J.G. Huneker, critic for the *New York World,* claimed, "Zaza in the role of Geraldine Farrar is a sensation. . . . She had taken possession of the physical habitation of Geraldine Farrar; therefore she was beautiful, therefore she was reborn with a golden throat. . . . There is only one role. She is Zaza. Zaza is Farrar." She was the first operatic luminary to acknowledge the existence of the motion pictures and capped her short career in that medium with a characterization of the savior of France in an epic entitled *Joan the Woman.* On 22 April 1922 she sang her last performance at the Metropolitan, an expectedly emotionally received Zaza, and then retired from the operatic stage at age forty, as she always said she would. She died in Ridgefield, Connecticut, 11 March 1967.

43. Geraldine Farrar
by Friedrich August von Kaulbach, 1904
Oil on canvas, 59 x 51
Lent by Library of Congress

Arturo Toscanini
1867-1957

Born in Parma, Italy, 25 March 1867, Arturo Toscanini was graduated from the Conservatory there in 1885 as a cellist, and as a cellist with a touring Italian opera company he first came to America. Pressed into service due to the indisposition of the regular conductor, Toscanini picked up the baton for the first time when he conducted Verdi's *Aïda* in Rio de Janeiro on 26 June 1886. He made his Italian debut as a conductor in Turin in the autumn of that same year. He was the conductor at the world premiere of Leoncavallo's *Pagliacci* in Milan on 22 May 1892 and for that of Giacomo Puccini's *La Bohème* in Turin on 1 February 1896. From 1898 he was chief conductor and music director of Milan's famed La Scala. By the time he was engaged as a conductor by the Metropolitan Opera he had acquired a reputation for both genius and irascibility. Verdi's *Aïda* was his first assignment in New York on 16 November 1908. One month later he conducted his first Wagnerian opera in the United States—*Götterdämmerung*—and amazed audiences and critics by conducting without a score. His tenure at the Metropolitan was during one of its "golden" ages. Sharing conducting duties with Gustav Mahler during his first season, he conducted Enrico Caruso, Emmy Destinn, Leo Slezak, Geraldine Farrar in performances that are now enshrined in the legends of operatic history in this country. On 10 December 1910 he conducted the premiere of Puccini's *La Fanciulla del West* before a glittering audience that included the composer and David Belasco, from whose play *The Girl of the Golden West* the operatic libretto had been adapted. Toscanini hurriedly left the Metropolitan at the end of the 1914–1915 season for reasons that have really never been fully explained. In 1920 and 1921 he returned to the United States with an orchestra touring under the auspices of La Scala. He returned again in 1926, when in Carnegie Hall on 14 January he appeared for the first time as a guest conductor with the New York Philharmonic Orchestra. Resigning from the opera house in Milan in 1929, Toscanini became the musical director of the Philharmonic and remained with it until 1936, building it into one of the world's great orchestras. Toscanini had been back in Italy only a short time when the National Broadcasting Company created an orchestra for him, and on 25 December 1937 he conducted the NBC Symphony for the first time. His radio audience—estimated at about 20,000,000—was undoubtedly the largest up to that time ever to hear a symphony concert in this country. On 11 May 1946 after eight years of self-imposed exile from Fascist Italy he returned to his liberated country to conduct the first concert on the newly restored stage of La Scala. In 1954, at age 87, Arturo Toscanini retired from the podium. He died in New York on 16 January 1957.

44. Arturo Toscanini
by Paul Troubetzkoy, before 1938
Bronze, 18 inches high
Lent by Mrs. Wanda Toscanini Horowitz

John Philip Sousa, born in Washington, D.C., on 6 November 1854, received his first musical instruction, on the violin and various band instruments, when he was six years old. At age fourteen when his father learned of his temptation to run away as a circus musician, the elder Sousa had him enlist in the United States Marine Band. After seven years he was discharged so that he might return to his studies. He began to write and to publish marches and galops and played with various theater and concert orchestras. In 1876 he was a violinist in Jacques Offenbach's orchestra at the centennial celebration in Philadelphia. He stayed in that city from 1876 until 1879 playing in the Chestnut Street Theatre and the Arch Street Theatre. For the Philadelphia Church Choir Company he wrote the first of his ten comic operas, *The Smugglers*. In September of 1880 he became the conductor of the United States Marine Band. His twelve-year association brought fame to both band and conductor. While with the Band he wrote two of his most popular marches, "Semper Fidelis" in 1888 and "The Washington Post" in the following year. In 1892 Sousa obtained backing for a band of his own, and with slow but steady success from the date of its first concert in Plainfield, New Jersey, on 26 September 1892 it achieved worldwide fame. The band played at the Chicago World's Columbian Exposition in 1893, toured Europe four times, and made a trip around the world in 1910 and 1911. For hundreds of thousands in this country and abroad, John Philip Sousa became the "March King." With his own marches, and arrangements of such popular songs as "After the Ball" and "Ta-ra-ra-boom-deay," Sousa also played music of the masters—Beethoven, Bach, and Wagner. He always attempted to achieve with his brass and woodwinds the refinement and precision of the full symphony orchestra. During the Spanish-American War, Sousa was the musical director of the Sixth Army Corps, and when he assumed charge of all United States Navy bands during World War I, he became the first ever to have had the distinction of directing the musical activities of all three branches of the military service. In an era of great band popularity in the United States—it is estimated that in 1899 there were perhaps 20,000— John Philip Sousa's musicianship and showmanship kept him at the forefront. After World War I, he reorganized his own band and during one seventeen-week concert tour in 1922 made $413,000. Royalties on his famed "Stars and Stripes Forever" written in 1897 are said to have been approximately $300,000. We would venture that next to "America," it is this country's most popular patriotic air and, as such, a fitting memorial to its composer. John Philip Sousa died in Reading, Pennsylvania, 6 March 1932.

45. John Philip Sousa
by Harry Waltman, 1909
Oil on canvas, 27 x 22
From the collection of the National Portrait Gallery

Ignace Paderewski first appeared in concert in the United States at Carnegie Hall on 17 November 1891. His bravura technique and his stage presence made him as much a favorite with American audiences as he had been with those in Paris and London. Even the hard-to-please English music critic George Bernard Shaw was moved to consider Paderewski the leading piano virtuoso of his time. In his first American tour he played 117 concerts. He was to return season after season from that time on and, in 1900, partly out of gratitude for his warm reception here, he created a fund of $10,000 to aid musical education in the United States. He was a composer as well as an instrumentalist, and his only opera, *Manru,* received its first American performance at the Metropolitan Opera House on 14 February 1902. The composer received fifteen curtain calls at the end of the first performance, but the New York critics gently panned the opera. After performances in five other American cities it was heard no more in the major opera houses of this country. Much more successful was Paderewski's *Symphony in B Minor* which had its world premiere by the Boston Symphony Orchestra on 12 February 1909. Composed on national themes, it illustrates clearly the inseparability of Paderewski's art and his politics. Having moved from Poland to Switzerland in 1899, Ignace Paderewski came to the United States at the outbreak of World War I, devoting all his energy and the proceeds from his concerts to Polish war relief. His efforts on behalf of his native country are considered a major factor in the creation of a free Poland at the end of the war. On 16 January 1919 he was nominated Prime Minister and Minister of Foreign Affairs of the new Republic of Poland, and it was he who represented his country at Versailles. Paderewski returned to the concert stage in 1923 and was greeted with enthusiasm by audiences everywhere. Music was again his major endeavor until the German invasion of Poland in 1939. On 23 January 1940 he was named President of the Polish National Council, the Polish government in exile in Paris. His efforts again were devoted totally to the cause of his oppressed country and he came to the United States for the last time in the same year to solicit aid for Poland. He died in New York on 29 June 1941 and at the request of President Franklin D. Roosevelt he was buried in Arlington National Cemetery.

46. Ignace Paderewski
by Charles E. Chambers, not dated
Oil on canvas, 30 x 30
Lent by Steinway & Sons

Anna Pavlova was ten years old when she was accepted into the Imperial School of Ballet in her native St. Petersburg, Russia, in 1891. She made her first stage appearance at a benefit for one of her teachers while still a student, and in 1899, upon completion of her training, was taken into the Imperial Ballet as a coryphée. By 1906 she was a prima ballerina. The following year she received a leave of absence to appear outside of Russia for the first time. She toured Europe for portions of three seasons and in 1909 appeared with the Diaghilev Ballets Russes during its Paris season. Her association with this revolutionary force in the history of ballet, however, was so short-lived as to have no effect upon her attitudes toward the dance, which were essentially those of a virtuoso dancer rather than a dance pioneer. In January of 1910 she appeared for the first time in America during a month-long season of ballet at the Metropolitan Opera House. She and her premier danseur, Mikhail Mordkin, were an immediate success, for it had been decades since the New York public had seen dancers of their caliber. She returned to the United States again in the season of 1910–1911 for an extensive tour and was already being written about as one who was to become a legendary figure in dance history. A critic of the *Boston Evening Times* reviewing her dancing of *The Dying Swan,* an incidental number danced to music from Camille Saint-Saëns' *Carnival of the Animals,* and a dance which was virtually her trademark, wrote, "Here was the dance of the phantom of a dream, stirring into misty and lingering vision, while out of flesh and blood, with imagination for the music and technical skill for the wand, Miss Pavlova wrought its gossamer beauty." Heady reporting, indeed. Anna Pavlova's personality and artistry entranced her audiences wherever she appeared, and she became a primary force in the popularization of ballet in the United States. Her role in the evolution of the modern dance was negligible, but her extended tours brought the dance in its classic beauty to millions who otherwise might never have discovered it. In 1913 she resigned from the company at St. Petersburg's Maryinsky Theatre and left Russia never to return. During the years of World War I she toured only in North and South America. From 1914 until 1930 she traveled with her company to almost every part of the civilized world. It is estimated that the sum total of her professional travels was well over 5,000,-000 miles. It can, indeed, be rightly said that Pavlova, among all the dancers of our century, did the most to open our world to ballet. During the midst of a European epidemic of influenza, Anna Pavlova died at The Hague in the Netherlands on 23 January 1931. She was cremated and her ashes were interred in London where she had resided since 1912. An American newspaper reporting her death looked back nostalgically and called her, "the fine flower of an age that was already passing when this lovely blossom appeared."

47. Anna Pavlova
by Malvina Hoffman, 1926
Terra cotta, 10½ inches high
Lent by The Corcoran Gallery of Art; Bequest of James Parmelee

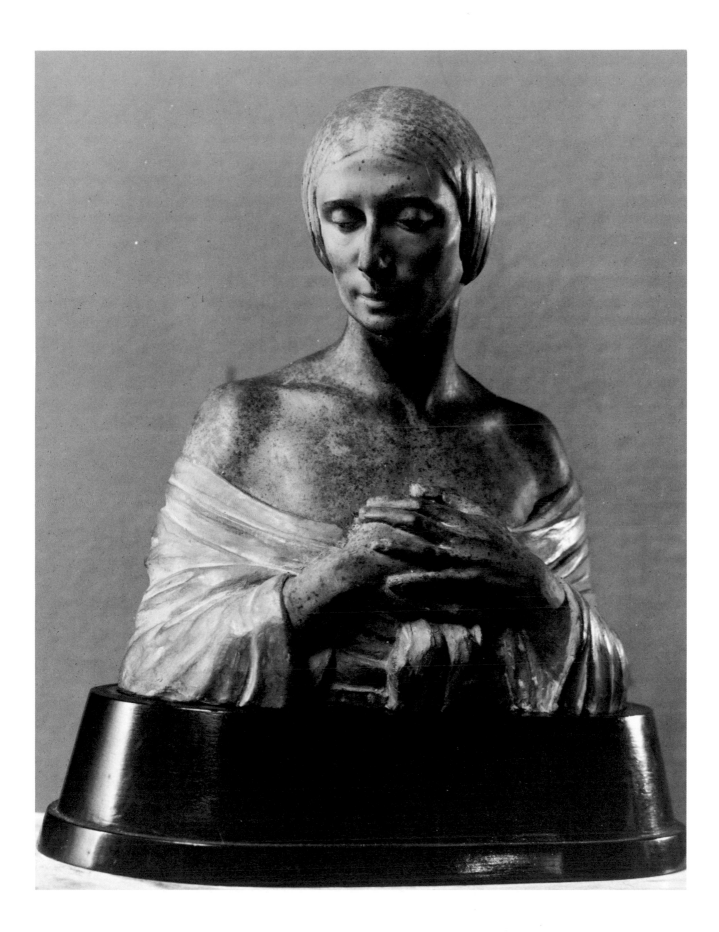

Vaslav Nijinsky
1890-1950

Born of Polish parents in Kiev, Russia, Vaslav Nijinsky was admitted to the school of the Imperial Ballet when he was nine and made his debut only after eight years of study. He became a member of the company at Moscow's Maryinsky Theatre, but his first great personal success came while he was on leave of absence from the Imperial Ballet and appearing in Paris with Serge Diaghilev's Ballets Russes in the spring of 1909. During a second Paris season the following year he was acclaimed as the greatest of the visiting Russian dancers. In 1911 Nijinsky was dismissed from the Imperial Ballet for appearing insufficiently clad before an audience that included the dowager empress. With Nijinsky free, Serge Diaghilev formed his ballet company into a permanent organization based in Western Europe rather than in Russia. During its first season in 1911 Nijinsky created two of the finest roles in his repertoire, the title roles of *Le Spectre de la Rose,* choreographed by Michel Fokine to music by Carl Maria von Weber, and *Petrouchka,* choreographed by Fokine to music by Igor Stravinsky. With Tamara Karsavina dancing the Young Girl to Nijinsky's Specter, *Le Spectre* was so enthusiastically received at one of its first performances at the Paris Opera that the entire ballet had to be repeated as an encore. During the following season Nijinsky made his first attempt to choreograph when he devised and staged *Afternoon of a Faun* to Claude Debussy's *Prélude a l'après-midi d'un faune.* At its first performance in Paris on 29 May 1912 the new ballet was enthusiastically received as much for its sexual element as for Nijinsky's superb dancing of the Faun. In 1913 Nijinsky visited South America with the Diaghilev company and was dismissed by the impresario when he married one of the dancers in the corps de ballet. During World War I, Vaslav Nijinsky, as a Russian subject, was held a civilian prisoner in his wife's home country, Austria-Hungary, and did not dance again until 1916. In that year, reconciled with Serge Diaghilev, he came to the United States for the first and only time on the second American tour of the Ballets Russes. He made his debut here on the stage of the Metropolitan Opera House on 12 April 1916 dancing a matinee of his two greatest roles, the Specter and Petrouchka, and danced in eleven of the twenty-eight performances of the short New York season. Neither the Diaghilev tour nor a second arranged by Nijinsky himself were outstanding successes. Knowing critics of the dance, however, perceived Vaslav Nijinsky for what he was—an artist whose personality and technique onstage could not be matched by any other male dancer of his time. Alexander Woollcott, always a demanding critic, is said to have included him in his personal five-deity Valhalla of performers—Eleonora Duse, Charlie Chaplin, Harpo Marx, Minnie Maddern Fiske, and Vaslav Nijinsky. In 1916 Nijinsky's mind began to show signs of a mental disease from which he never recovered. He danced for the last time in Switzerland in 1919 and entered the first of a long succession of mental institutions. He died in London on 8 April 1950 unaware, perhaps, that he had become a legend and a personification of the dance.

48. Vaslav Nijinsky in the title role of the ballet *Le Dieu Bleu*
by Malvina Hoffman, 1920
Bronze, 10¾ inches high
Lent by Robert L. B. Tobin

Ruth St. Denis
1877-1968

Ted Shawn
1891-

Ruth Denis began her dancing career about 1894 by auditioning in the foyer of Worth's Museum on Sixth Avenue in New York before a rather astonished ticket seller. She got a job and a two-week engagement of eleven performances a day. By 1899 she was off to London doing a bit part in *Zaza,* directed by David Belasco. It was while in one of Belasco's productions, and most certainly on a day when he was affecting clerical grab, that he elevated her to "St. -hood." A cigarette poster with an Egyptian theme suggested a whole new concept of dance theater to her, and slowly, but definitely, she began evolving a repertory of dances based on Oriental themes. Her success in New York and Boston was moderate compared to her achievement in Europe. After a slow start in Boston she made major headlines after her debut at the Marigny in Paris, 1 September 1906. Hers was an even greater triumph in Berlin; in Vienna the poet Hugo von Hofmannsthal called her dancing "incomparable." London was more enthusiastic the second time around, and when she returned home in 1909 she came back a major American star. She had already won a place for herself as the third person of the dance trinity of the twentieth century—Loie Fuller, Isadora Duncan, and Ruth St. Denis. Ted Shawn was a young ministerial student when he first saw Ruth St. Denis dance in Denver in 1911. He was rather overcome by what he saw. He had begun dancing in his junior year in college, as physical therapy to counteract the effects of a paralysis from an attack of diphtheria. In 1914, within days after first approaching her to be her pupil, he was hired as her dance partner. They danced together onstage for the first time in Paducah, Illinois on 13 April 1914 and on 13 August they were married. Their first joint choreography, *The Garden of Kama,* was danced in February of 1915. An estimate of their increasing popularity with American audiences can be documented in the fact that their portrait in costume was among the earliest color plates in the magazine that ranks next only to the Holy Bible in most American homes—*The National Geographic.* In the same year they founded in California the Denshawn School, an important nursery for the nurturing of the younger generation of American dancers. World War I interrupted the duo-career while Shawn served in the Army. Between 1922 and 1925 there was a series of most successful American tours. In the autumn of 1925 St. Denis and Shawn and company departed on a year-and-a-half tour of the Orient. They were applauded wherever they appeared and were accepted as eloquent evidence that America did indeed have culture as well as money. Returning home in the spring of 1927, they found themselves of sufficient stature to badger the New York newspapers into creating posts for dance critics. Two such talents under one roof understandably led to discontent, and in 1931 they did not divorce but went their separate ways except for some concert dates together. Shawn, after teaching at Springfield College for a short while in 1932 and 1933, founded his internationally lauded

49. Ruth St. Denis in her *Kwannon* dance
by Albert Herter, 1925
Oil on canvas, 90 x 40
Lent by Ted Shawn

50. Ted Shawn in his *Thunderbird* dance
by Albert Herter, 1925
Oil on canvas, 90 x 40
Lent by Ted Shawn

group, Ted Shawn and his Men Dancers. He had made the dance respectable as a profession for men. They toured for seven years, giving over 1,200 performances in 750 cities. He obtained property in western Massachusetts, and from a lecture-demonstration session in July of 1933 evolved the facilities into the site of one of the nation's foremost dance institutions. The annual summer Jacob's Pillow Dance Festival really began in 1942 with the opening of the Ted Shawn Theatre. Over a thousand dancers and dance companies have appeared there since, many making their American debuts. More than two hundred and fifty world premieres of choreographic works have occurred there. "Miss Ruth," as she was affectionately called by those who loved her, made a comeback in 1937 after some years in shadow. In 1940 she opened her St. Denis School of Natya in New York, and in 1941 she danced at the Jacob's Pillow Dance Festival, a program duplicating a significant early success at New York's Hudson Theater thirty-five years before. At Jacob's Pillow in 1964 St. Denis and Shawn danced their last new duet together, Siddhas of the Upper Air, in celebration of their golden wedding anniversary.

Isadora Duncan
1878-1927

Six years after her birth in San Francisco on 28 May 1878, Isadora Duncan exhibited the first signs of her artistic precocity by teaching dancing to the children of her neighborhood. At age seventeen she and her mother traveled to Chicago and New York where impresarios had little enthusiasm for the young dancer's "new system" of interpretive dancing. Off to London by cattle boat, the entire Duncan family was discovered by the actress Mrs. Patrick Campbell and introduced to a more appreciative audience. By the time Isadora returned to the United States in 1906 her creative new dance form had been applauded by private audiences in London and Paris, she had been for a while with Loie Fuller's touring company, and she had made a triumphant solo tour of Munich, Berlin, Vienna, and Budapest. She had also attempted to build a temple of dance on a hill outside Athens and in 1904 opened a dancing school in the Berlin suburb of Grünewald. Isadora looked to antiquity as the inspiration for her dancing. When she returned for another American tour in late summer of 1908 the press accepted her dances as "classical," a reviewer in the *New York Sun* on 29 August calling her "the young woman who stepped down from a Grecian vase in the British Museum." No matter how fetching her movement onstage may have been, there were constant criticisms of her insistence on dancing to music not intended for the dance. Carl Van Vechten, in his *New York Times* review of her performance at the Metropolitan Opera House on 17 November 1909, protested against her "perverted use" of Beethoven's *Seventh Symphony* and in February of 1911 was still wondering why she insisted on dancing to music such as the "Liebestod" from Wagner's *Tristan und Isolde*. The artist John Sloan greatly admired her and saw this same performance on 15 February 1911. A portion of his diary entry for the day is both honest and enthusiastic:

Isadora as she appears on that big simple stage seems like all womanhood—she looms big as the mother of the race. A heavy solid figure, large columnar legs, a solid high belly, breasts not too full and her head seems to be no more important than it should to give the body the chief place. In one of the dances she was absolutely nude save for a thin gauze drapery hanging from the shoulders. In none was she much clothed, simple filmy coverings usually with a loin cloth.

From *John Sloan's New York Scene,* edited by
Bruce St. John, courtesy of Harper & Row, Publishers, Inc.

Hers was one of the most original and creative contributions to twentieth-century dance, and she generally found her audiences appreciative of her efforts. Tours of South America in 1916 and of this country again in 1917, however, were relatively unsuccessful, and she returned to Europe. In 1921 she accepted an invitation of the Soviet government to open a school in Moscow. She married there in 1922 the poet Sergei Yessenin, and and when she returned to America with him they were suspected of being Bolshevist propagandists. Her last trip here a failure, she bid farewell to an America she said knew

51. Isadora Duncan
by John Sloan, 1911
Oil on canvas, 32¼ x 26¼
Lent by Milwaukee Art Center, Gift of Mr. and Mrs. Donald B. Abert

nothing of "Love, Food, or Art," and she vowed never to return. In Paris in 1925 Yessenin committed suicide. The next two years were artistically barren for Isadora except for the writing and publication of her forthright biography, *My Life*. Its publication came just in time. At Nice, France, on 14 September 1927 she stepped into a sports car to go for a ride with a friend. The long scarf she was wearing caught in the back wheel of the car and she was garroted.

Walter Hampden
1879-1955

Born in Brooklyn on 30 June 1879, Walter Hampden Dougherty made one of his first appearances onstage there as Shylock in a Brooklyn Polytechnic Institute production when he was sixteen-years old. He dropped his family name for stage purposes and went to England for his theatrical apprenticeship, making his debut at Brighton on 2 September 1901. Three years later he was acting with the repertory company at London's Adelphi Theatre and in May of 1905 replaced Sir Henry Irving for one week in the role of Hamlet. Returning to New York he was engaged by Henry Miller to support Alla Nazimova and first appeared with her on 2 September 1907 as Count Silvio in *The Comtesse Couquette.* In the same season he appeared with her in *The Master Builder* and in *A Doll's House.* In March of 1908 Hampden created the role of Manson in Charles Rann Kennedy's *The Servant in the House.* In 1916, the tercentenary of Shakespeare's death, he played Calibran in a notable revival of *The Tempest.* He was at his peak two years later when in March and April of 1918 he played Elihu in *The Book of Job,* Jokanaan in Oscar Wilde's *Salome,* and Marc Antony and Oberon in more familiar works by Shakespeare. On 22 November 1918 he opened at the Plymouth Theatre in *Hamlet.* Critic Clayton Hamilton, claiming he had seen all the Hamlets on the English-speaking stage since Edwin Booth, called Hampden the greatest living interpreter of the "Melancholy Dane." Shylock, the role of his erstwhile debut in his teens, was added to his professional repertory while on tour in 1920. Rostand's long-nosed, but romantic hero Cyrano de Bergerac became another of his great characterizations when he opened at New York's National Theatre in a new version by Brian Hooker on 1 November 1923. It was played 250 performances in that house before he took it on tour. In 1925 he leased the Colonial Theatre and, renaming it Hampden's Theatre, opened in *Hamlet* with Ethel Barrymore as his Ophelia. Two years later he became the fourth president of The Players, succeeding Edwin Booth, Joseph Jefferson, and John Drew. Although by tradition an office held for life, Walter Hampden relinquished the title on 8 October 1954. He made his first appearance on television as Macbeth in the Hallmark Playhouse production and appeared for the last time on Broadway as Deputy-Governor Danforth in Arthur Miller's *The Crucible* in October 1953. In Hollywood to make a motion picture, he was stricken while on his way to the Metro-Goldwyn-Mayer studios and died in Cedars of Lebanon Hospital on 11 June 1955.

52. Walter Hampden in the title role of Shakespeare's *Hamlet*
by William Glackens, circa 1918
Oil on canvas; 75½ x 40
From the collection of the National Portrait Gallery

Born in Yalta, Russia, on 4 June 1879, Alla Nazimova was a music student for a short time before she entered the Academy of Acting in Moscow. In 1904 she joined the theatrical company of Paul Orleneff and toured with it, making her New York debut on 23 March 1905 in a Russian language production of Chirikov's *The Chosen People.* The American portion of their tour a failure, the company returned to Russia, but Nazimova remained behind. On 13 November 1906 she made her English language debut at the Princess Theatre in Ibsen's *Hedda Gabler.* She followed close on the heels of Mrs. Fiske as a champion of the Norwegian dramatist. In 1907 she appeared in *A Doll's House* and in *The Master Builder* with Walter Hampden. In 1910 she was first seen in *Little Eyolf.* It was her appearances in what one critic called her "lust-and-vengeance-dramas" such as *Comet, The Passion Flower,* and *Bella Donna* that first really claimed the attention of the American public. Between 1916 and 1923 she appeared in a number of motion pictures which included *A Doll's House, Camille,* and a famed production of Oscar Wilde's *Salome* designed à la Beardsley by Natacha Rambova. In 1918 Nazimova received special acclaim for a series of three Ibsen plays, which added *The Wild Duck* to revivals of *Hedda Gabler* and the inevitable *A Doll's House.* An undisputed high point of her career was her creation of the role of Christine in the Theatre Guild production of Eugene O'Neill's *Mourning Becomes Electra* which premiered in New York on 26 October 1931. Robert Benchley in his review of the first performance wrote, "Nazimova, in spite of her Russian accent . . . made so much of the sinning Clytemnestra (Christine) that the drama lost much when she withdrew into the shade of the House of Mannon never to return." Her acting of Mrs. Alving in her touring production of Ibsen's *Ghosts* in the 1935-1936 season prompted some critics to compare her with Duse. The title role in *Hedda Gabler* was now considered her property and she opened her fourth and last run in the drama at the Longacre Theatre on 16 November 1936. When it closed she had, as the ill-fated Hedda, committed suicide on Broadway 128 times. She was last seen on the New York stage in April of 1939 in *The Mother.* Her artistic endeavors shifted again to the cinema. She died in Hollywood 13 July 1945.

53. Alla Nazimova
by Edward Simmons, 1915
Oil on canvas, 24 x 24
Lent by Dr. Henry Harvitt

Fay Bainter
1892-1968

Born in Los Angeles on 7 December 1892, Fay Bainter made her stage debut at age six in a stock company production of a play called *The Jewess*. After further appearance in stock, musical repertory, and vaudeville, she made her New York debut as Celine in *The Rose of Panama* at Daly's Theatre on 22 January 1912. Her first hit was as the Japanese princess, an idol which came to life in *The Willow Tree*. The play evidently was not a great one, but the critics liked Miss Bainter. The day after the opening on 6 March 1917 at the Cohan and Harris Theatre, the *New York Times* review carried the headline, "Fay Bainter Acts with Rare Tenderness and Witchery a Play Now Overlong and Overtricky." Artist Robert Henri preserved her appearance in this role in a charming painting and admired her as well in the next production in which she starred. Of her first appearance in *The Kiss Burglar,* 9 May 1918, he wrote to a friend in Toledo, "Last night Fay Bainter was a delight to us and all the rest of the audience . . . She put beauty into musical comedy, and I hope she has put it there to stay." She achieved stardom in another oriental role in *East is West* which opened in New York on Christmas Day 1918 and later toured until 1922. In 1927 she made another cross-country tour in a vaudeville presentation entitled *Great Moments in Great Plays*. Special acclaim came her way for her performances in *Lysistrata, For Services Rendered,* and *Dodsworth* in the early thirties. She never aspired to Shakespeare, but some of her characterizations were cast from the classic mold of tragedy. She played Amanda in Tennessee Williams' *The Glass Menagerie* for the first time in 1955 at Houston's Alley Theatre, and she was Mary Cavan Tyrone in the touring company of O'Neill's *Long Day's Journey into Night* in the season of 1957-1958. Among her numerous motion-picture roles the most notable was that of Auntie Belle in *Jezebel,* which won her an Academy Award in 1938. She died April 16 1968.

54. Fay Bainter as the Willow Princess
in Benrimo and Harrison Rhodes' *The Willow Tree*
by Robert Henri, 1918
Oil on canvas, 66⅛ x 45

Lent anonymously through the courtesy of Hirschl and Adler Galleries

Otis Skinner
1858–1942

The son and grandson of Universalist ministers, Otis Skinner was born in Cambridge, Massachusetts, on 28 June 1858. Disdaining to follow the family calling, he began his theatrical career with the acting company of the Philadelphia Museum on 30 October 1877 as Jim, an old Negro, in Phillip Stoner's *Woodleigh*. In his first season of apprenticeship he played ninety-two characters. Although his first New York appearance was made supporting John McCullough in *Coriolanus,* he considered his real debut in that city his appearance as Maclow in *Enchantment* first produced at Niblo's Gardens on 4 September 1879. He supported Edwin Booth and Lawrence Barrett for a while and for three years was a member of Augustin Daly's company. In 1894 he produced and starred in what was to be the first romantic role favored by his public, *His Grace de Grammont* by Clyde Fitch. Physically and temperamentally endowed to be an ideal romantic hero, Otis Skinner remained popular with his audiences by the happy coincidence of his greatest roles. In 1907 Broadway saw him in the comic part of Colonel Philippe Bridau in *The Honor of the Family,* and he achieved his greatest fame in the role of Hajj in *Kismet* by Edward Knoblock. After playing the role for three years in New York and on tour, he made a silent film version of the play and still later a sound version. His career onstage lasted fifty-eight years and encompassed 325 parts. He outlived Edwin Booth by fifty years and was therefore one of the last of the American actors trained in the traditions of the nineteenth century, traditions of versatility and the grand manner. His style was at odds with the major developments in the theater in the first years of this century, and his undiminished popularity up until the time of his retirement must be taken as a tribute to his talents. His last appearance was as Uncle Tom in a 1933 revival of *Uncle Tom's Cabin.* He died in New York on 4 January 1942.

55. Otis Skinner as Colonel Bridau in *The Honor of the Family*
by George Luks, 1919
Oil on canvas, 52 x 44
Lent by the Phillips Collection

Feodor Chaliapin made his operatic debut at age seventeen with a provincial opera company in his native Russia. In 1901, after having acquired somewhat of a reputation for himself in Moscow as a singing actor, he sang outside of Russia for the first time. He first appeared in New York at the Metropolitan Opera 20 November 1907 in the title role of Arrigo Boito's *Mefistofele*. So rattled was Henry Krehbiel, the critic of the *New York Tribune,* by Chaliapin's acting and costuming of the role, that he never once mentioned the singer's voice. Cultured New York was more than slightly overcome by what it considered the crudeness and carnality of Chaliapin's handling of the devilish role. In defense of New York it must be said that not that city alone found fault with the Russian singer's characterization in this as well as in other Italian and French operas. However masterful the characterizations might have been they were incompatible with tradition and therefore not immediately acceptable. In the opera of his homeland, however, it was a different matter, and he became truly worthy of being the first Russian singer to win international fame when he appeared as the guilty, soul-tormented hero of Modest Mussorgsky's *Boris Godunov*. New York first heard him in this role on 9 December 1921. Henry Krehbiel's review of this performance was filled with superlatives, "Centenarians with memories stored away with recollections of Kean, Macready, and Forrest (if there be any such alive) might have attended a performance of *Boris Godounoff* (sic) at the Metropolitan Opera House last night and felt such swelling of the heart as they experienced when tragedy was at its prime in New York . . . Last night nobility of acting was paired with a beautiful nobility of voice and vocal style." He remained with the Metropolitan through the season of 1928-1929, his last performance with the company being as Méphistophélès in Gounod's *Faust* on 20 March 1929. His was an irrepressible personality. He defied the Met management's ban on encores when he thought his public expected them, and when singing in concert halls he made up his program as he went along. No programs were given out at his recitals. The audience had to purchase books which contained the texts of all the songs in his repertoire and he announced his selections as he made them. Self-exiled from Russia, he died in Paris on 12 April 1938.

56. Feodor Chaliapin in the title role of
Modest Mussorgsky's *Boris Godunov*
by Boris Chaliapin
Polychromed plaster, 28 inches high
Lent by the Artist

Jeanne Eagels
1890-1929

Born in the Midwest on 26 June 1890, Jeanne Eagels came into show business by way of a touring Dubinsky Brothers' tent show when she was fifteen. By the time she made it to New York, impresario David Belasco described her eyes as "hard and bitter, but shining with ambition." She first attracted the attention of Broadway theatergoers when she appeared as Miss Renault in the 1911 production of a play entitled *Jumping Jupiter*. Most of the plays in which she appeared are now mentioned only in the most scholarly anthologies of Broadway productions. One was notable, however—a revival of *Disraeli* in which she played under George Arliss in his most famous role, and she had a 340-performance run beginning on 5 September 1918 when she opened in *Daddies* at the Belasco Theatre. These plays are all overshadowed, however, by her one spectacular triumph. At Maxine Elliott's Theatre on 7 November 1922 she created the role of Sadie Thompson in John Colton's and Clemence Randolph's adaptation of Somerset Maugham's story, *Miss Thompson*. The play, and Jeanne Eagels as the wayward prostitute Sadie, were the dramatic triumphs of the 1922–1923 New York season. John Corbin's *New York Times* review of the opening-night performance on 7 November 1922 described Miss Eagels' acting as having "an emotional power as fiery and unbridled in effect as it is artistically restrained," and noted that "The house . . . fairly rose to Miss Eagels and acclaimed her." *Rain* played for 648 performances. The remainder of her career was downhill. On 21 March 1927 she opened in *Her Cardboard Lover* at the Empire Theatre for 152 performances. The next season the play went on tour. She failed to appear at a performance in Milwaukee and in St. Louis; four days later she left the show, forcing the producers to cancel the remainder of the tour. Early in April of 1928 Actor's Equity Association barred her from the stage. She ruined both her health and her career through overindulgence in alcohol and drugs, and on 3 October 1929 she collapsed and died at the Park Avenue Hospital during a routine physical examination.

57. Jeanne Eagels as Sadie Thompson in
John Colton's and Clemence Randolph's *Rain*
by Guy Pene du Bois, 1922
Oil on canvas, 84¾ x 48
Lent by Whitney Museum of American Art

John Barrymore
1882-1942

The inheritor of generations of theatrical tradition, John Barrymore did not originally want to be an actor. He really wanted to be a painter and it was only after unsuccessful attempts as a painter and illustrator that he like his older sister Ethel turned to the stage. The tales of his erratic behavior onstage and offstage in the years of his apprenticeship reflect the lack of seriousness in his calling in the early days. His first appearance onstage was as a substitute for an indisposed actor during the Philadelphia tryout of his sister's first great hit *Captain Jinks of the Horse Marines*. He muffed his lines but, unabashed, he took a solo curtain call. As befitted his attitude, most of his early roles were in a lighter vein. His first substantial role was as Max in a production of Hermann Sudermann's *Magda* in Chicago in October of 1903. Two months later he played New York for the first time when he opened at the Savoy Theatre as Corley in *Glad of It*. He matured a bit as an actor when he opened as Charley Hine in Richard Harding Davis' *The Dictator* at New York's Criterion Theatre on 4 April 1904. He played his first major role in Rida Johnson Young's *The Boys of Company B* in the spring of 1907 and the only musical role of his career in *A Stubborn Cinderella* early in 1909. On 4 September 1909 he opened in New York as Nat Duncan in Winchell Smith's *The Fortune Hunter* and found himself a star. In 1916 he made his first venture into serious dramatic acting when he appeared in John Galsworthy's *Justice,* both in New York and on tour. His birth as a romantic star came with his first appearance in the title role of John Raphael's *Peter Ibbetson* which premiered at the Republic Theatre on 17 April 1917. With him in the cast was his older brother Lionel. In 1819 he appeared in a revival of Leo Tolstoi's *Redemption* which ran on Broadway for 204 performances. The following year he appeared again opposite his brother in *The Jest,* by Sam Benelli. With painstaking thoroughness John Barrymore prepared for his first Shakespeare, *Richard III,* in 1920. He put himself in the hands of an able coach to prepare his voice and his delivery of the lengthy verse passages. The costuming of his Richard was meticulous. He had two suits of full-weight armor made to order and he conferred with experts at the British Museum regarding the design of the armor and a sword he was to carry onstage. He considered the role of the deformed king the first "genuine acting" he had done. Dramatically, it was one of the two pinnacles of his career. The second, even loftier, was his reading of the melancholy Prince of Denmark. John Barrymore's *Hamlet* opened at the Sam H. Harris Theatre on 16 November 1922. In his review in the *Herald* the following day, Alexander Woollcott gave the venture his pontifical blessing when he wrote, "One who has seen all the *Hamlets* that have been given in this country in the last twenty-five years must give over the very front of his report to the conviction that this new one is the finest of them all." The critic of the *Evening Post* found the play, "Gorgeously dressed and mounted by Arthur Hopkins, but tamely acted by John Barrymore and his associates . . ." The public

58. John Barrymore in the title role of Shakespeare's *Hamlet*
by James Montgomery Flagg, circa 1923
Oil on canvas, 40 x 50
Lent by Museum of the City of New York, Theatre and Music Collection

obviously sided with Woollcott, for the play ran for 102 performances, one more than the legendary run by Edwin Booth and one less, unfortunately, than that of John E. Kellard which was the undisputed winner in the Hamlet marathon from 1912 to 1961. In 1925 John Barrymore left the stage to devote all his time to work in motion pictures where his famed profile became one of the shining ornaments of the silver screen. He returned to the stage only once, in 1939 in *My Dear Children,* to play a character who was a pathetic caricature of himself in his declining years. He died in Hollywood on 29 May 1942.

The daughter of a medical student from Buffalo, Katharine Cornell was born in Berlin, Germany, on 16 February 1898. Her New York stage debut was made as a Japanese mother in the Washington Square Players' production of *Bushido* at the Comedy Theatre, 13 November 1916. Her entire part consisted of only four words. Other minor roles followed before she joined a stock company which played Buffalo and Detroit. After a half dozen ingénue parts she played her first lead role in a 1915 production of *The Man Who Came Back,* and on 20 November 1919 she made her London debut in a dramatization of Louisa May Alcott's *Little Women.* Returning home, she played Diane in *Seventh Heaven* in Detroit and returned to New York in 1921. She had her first real personal triumph when she played Sydney Fairfield in Clemence Dane's *Bill of Divorcement* that same year, and her name went up in lights when she opened as Iris March in Michael Arlen's *The Green Hat* at the Broadhurst Theatre on 15 September 1925. On 12 December 1924 she opened at the 48th Street Theatre in the title role of George Bernard Shaw's *Candida.* Reviewing the opening-night performance in the *New York Times,* Stark Young said, "Candida in the hands of Katharine Cornell was a deep revelation of the part. Her frail presence had something in it of the light of another world." Heywood Broun in the *World* wrote, "The Candida of Katharine Cornell is the finest performance she has yet given for our theatre. It is bright with a steady flame. It is beautiful to look at and beautiful to feel." Each season after that she returned to Broadway and added to her laurels. From 1931 she appeared only under her own management. On 9 February 1931 she opened at the Empire Theatre as Elizabeth Barrett in Rudolf Besier's *The Barretts of Wimpole Street,* which ran 372 performances and toured until July of 1932. This role became a staple in her repertory and she played it again on tour in the season of 1933–1934, alternating it with *Candida* and *Romeo and Juliet,* which Brooks Atkinson called a "stunning production." In February of 1935 she opened again in New York as Elizabeth Barrett. She added another Shaw play to her credits when she played his *St. Joan* for the first time in March of 1936. In 1937 and 1942 she again revived *Candida* and during the war years toured with *The Barretts of Wimpole Street* in performances for military audiences in Europe. On 26 November 1947 she added another sterling characterization of a Shakespeare heroine to her checklist of successes when she opened at the Martin Beck Theatre in *Antony and Cleopatra* for the longest run the play had ever had, 126 performances. In the season of 1951–1952 she appeared in a notable revival of *The Constant Wife* by Somerset Maugham, and in 1959 and 1960 on tour and in New York, she played an actress of an earlier era, Mrs. Patrick Campbell, in *Dear Liar.* She has received many honors during her long and distinguished career. Among them, are the Freedom Medal, a medal from the American Academy of Arts and Letters, and eleven honorary doctorates from colleges and universities.

59. Katharine Cornell in the title role of George Bernard Shaw's *Candida*
by Eugene Speicher, 1926
Oil on canvas, 83 4/5 x 45½
Lent by Albright-Knox Gallery, Buffalo, New York

When he was three years old, Clifton Webb and his family moved to New York from Indianapolis, where he was born on 19 November 1893. By way of a dancing class he made his stage debut in 1900 as Cholly in a Carnegie Hall children's theatrical entitled *The Brownies*. In the next production of the same small company he had a title role, that of Oliver Twist in a dramatization of the Dickens novel. Leaving school he studied painting with Robert Henri and voice with the baritone Victor Maurel. In his teens he made his operatic debut as Laertes in Boston in a production of Ambroise Thomas' *Mignon*. On 7 April 1913 Clifton Webb appeared in his first light opera in New York when he opened in *The Purple Road* at Maxine Elliott's Theatre for a run of 136 performances. For a while he was a partner to Bonnie Glass and later to Mae Murray and became second in popularity as a ballroom dancer only to the famed duo of Irene and Vernon Castle. His first appearance on Broadway in a musical was in Cole Porter and T. Lawrason Riggs' *See America First*, a spoof on George M. Cohan flag-waving shows. It did not find favor with a flag-waving public and lasted only fifteen performances. A series of shows between 1917 and 1921, *Love O'Mike, Listen Lester,* and *As You Were,* found him fully established in his audiences' favor as a dancer. Two successful seasons in London and Paris followed, and then Clifton Webb returned to New York in John Murray Anderson's *Jack and Jill,* which opened a ninety-two-performance run at the Globe Theatre on 22 March 1923. Later the same year he played his first straight comedy role in *Meet the Wife* at the Klaw Theatre. George F. Kaufman in reviewing it stated, "Mr. Webb will never have to put on his dancing shoes again." He did, however, when he appeared in the musical *Sunny* at the New Amsterdam Theatre in the fall and winter of 1925 and in a number of shows in which he starred in the next eight years. Notable among them were Rodgers and Hart's *She's My Baby* and George Gershwin's *Treasure Girl* in 1928, *Three's a Crowd* in 1930, and *Flying Colors* in 1932. Opening at the Music Box Theatre on 30 September 1933 in Moss Hart and Irving Berlin's *As Thousands Cheer,* Webb gave a bravura performance alongside cohorts Ethel Waters and Marilyn Miller and then returned to the West Coast for his first stay in Hollywood. In the entire eighteen months he was there—under a contract paying a reported $3,000 a week—he never made one movie. Back he went to Broadway for a nondancing role, opening on 12 October 1936 at the Guild Theatre in *And Stars Remain.* In 1939 he starred in an important revival of Oscar Wilde's *The Importance of Being Ernest;* he followed its run with a year and a half on tour as Sheridan Whitesides in Moss Hart and George Kaufman's satire on critic Alexander Woollcott, *The Man Who Came to Dinner.* On the eve of World War II he opened at the Morosco Theatre as the harassed hero of Noel Coward's *Blithe Spirit,* which gave a sadly needed touch of lightness to a trying time and ran for 650 performances. Most of his talent from that time on was exhibited for the benefit of Hollywood motion-picture cameras. A notable return to Broadway was in *Present Laughter,* which opened at the Plymouth Theatre on 29 October 1946. Clifton Webb died on 13 October 1966 in Beverly Hills.

60. Clifton Webb
by Walter Dean Goldbeck, before 1925
Oil on canvas, 50 x 40
Lent by Museum of City of New York, Theatre and Music Collection

Leopold Stokowski
1882-

Born in London, Leopold Stokowski studied there and on the Continent and first came to the United States in 1905 to be organist of St. Bartholomew's Church in New York. In 1909 he became the conductor of the Cincinnati Symphony Orchestra and during his tenure took it on a tour of the West, one of the first by an orchestra that that section of the country had ever known. In 1912 he became the conductor of the Philadelphia Orchestra and built it into one of the foremost musical organizations in the world. His policy of introducing the most advanced music often brought hisses from his audiences, and he in turn did not hesitate to turn around on the podium to criticize such concert hall misbehavior. His use of colored lights during concerts and his decision to conduct without a baton also caused much comment by audience and press. In 1922 he was the first recipient of Philadelphia's Edward Bok award for most valuable service to that city. Notable among the works which he introduced to American audiences were Gustav Mahler's *Eighth Symphony,* which the Orchestra played for the first time in the spring of 1916, and Alban Berg's *Wozzeck,* which Stokowski conducted for the Philadelphia Grand Opera on 19 March 1931. In 1933 he introduced concerts designed especially for audiences fifteen to twenty-five years old. His announcement of resignation in the winter of 1934 caused a great furor and ended with Mr. Stokowski being granted the final authority in all matters of policy. At the end of the 1936–1937 season he actually did resign but continued to conduct occasionally through the season of 1940–1941. In 1940 he also organized the All-American Youth Orchestra and took it on a goodwill tour of South America. A second orchestra of the same type, limited to instrumentalists between the ages of fifteen and twenty-five, toured the United States the following year. After leaving Philadelphia, Mr. Stokowski devoted much of his time to radio and motion pictures, in which he had appeared as early as 1936, and to guest conducting. During World War II he was adviser to the United States Army on bands and band music. In 1944, at the invitation of Mayor Fiorello La Guardia, he organized the New York City Symphony and conducted it through the season of 1944–1945. From 1946 until 1949 he was a guest conductor with the New York Philharmonic and with Dimitri Mitropoulos, regular co-conductor, during the 1949–1950 season. Notable among Maestro Stokowski's most recent appearances have been his conducting of the first full-scale concert ever held in New York's St. Patrick's Cathedral on 29 November 1970 and his concerts with the American Symphony Orchestra which he founded in 1962.

61. Leopold Stokowski
by Leopold Seyffert, 1916
Charcoal on paper, 20 x 16
From the collection of the National Portrait Gallery

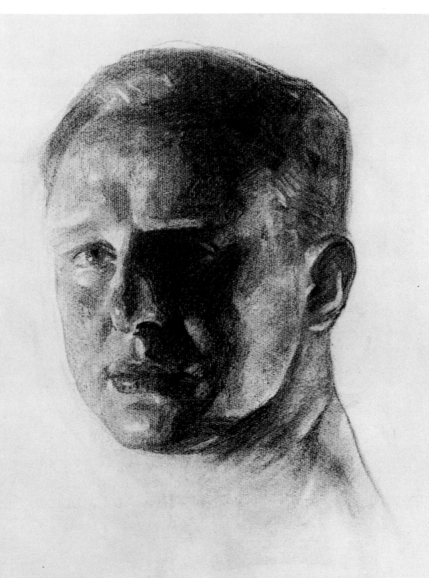

Leopold Seyffert
1916 ©

Tallulah Bankhead
1902–1968

Tallulah Bankhead got into show business by winning a *Pictureplay* photo contest in 1917. She made her New York stage debut at the Bijou Theatre on 13 March 1918 as Mary Sinclair in *The Squab Farm.* For the next four years she walked through a series of ingénue roles and then took off to London where she appeared for the first time as Maxine in *The Dancers,* opening at Wyndham's Theatre on 15 February 1923. Her popularity and fame grew and by October of 1929, when she opened as Wanda Myro in Arthur Wimperis' adaption of Louis Verneuil's *He's Mine,* the noted painter Augustus John was begging her to sit for him. She did, and the result was a portrait that was a hit when exhibited at the Royal Academy and Miss Bankhead's prize possession until her death. Returning to the United States with considerably more of a professional reputation than when she left, she made a few movies for Paramount and then returned to the New York stage as Mary Clay, the jilted bride, in Edward Roberts and Frank Cavett's *Forsaking All Others,* opening at the Times Square Theatre on 1 March 1933. She was affectionately received by opening-night audiences, and the play lasted 101 performances. After a short tour in *The Snob,* she opened again in New York at the Music Box on 12 February 1935 as Sadie Thompson in a revival of *Rain.* Still remembering Jeanne Eagles in the role, some of the critics found Miss Bankhead's characterization fuzzy, others, like Robert Garland, critic of the New York *Telegram,* found Miss Bankhead "superb." Several characterizations later, in November of 1937, there was unanimous agreement that she had flopped miserably as Cleopatra in Shakespeare's *Antony and Cleopatra.* John Mason Brown's criticism, "Miss Bankhead barged down the aisle as Cleopatra and sank. As the serpent of the Nile she proved to be no more dangerous than a garter snake," being the most notable memento of the production. On 15 February 1939 she opened at the National Theatre as Regina Giddins in Lillian Hellman's *The Little Foxes,* which she and many of her critics and admirers considered her finest role. The play ran on Broadway for 410 performances. A prize-winning performance followed soon after when she played Sabina in Thornton Wilder's *The Skin of Our Teeth* during the 1942–1943 Broadway season. Other noteworthy roles on her full career were Blanche DuBois in a revival of Tennessee Williams' *Streetcar Named Desire,* which played at New York City Center early in 1956, and the title role in *Midge Purvis,* which opened at the Martin Beck Theatre 1 February 1961. Her sense of humor toward her profession and toward her own capabilities and failings was nowhere more evident than in her autobiography, aptly and succinctly called *Tallulah,* published in 1952, omitting, unfortunately, her last years. Late in her career, but with full awareness of her drawing power and with tongue only slightly in cheek, she made an appearance as a villainess in the television *Batman* series. The curtain came down only when she died on 12 December 1968.

62. Tallulah Bankhead as Wanda Myro in Arthur Wimperis' *He's Mine*
by Augustus John, 1930
Oil on canvas, 48 x 24½
From the collection of the National Portrait Gallery

Martha Graham
1900?-

Born in Pittsburgh, Martha Graham grew up in Santa Barbara, California. In 1916 she began studies at the Denishawn School of the Dance in Los Angeles and studied with both Ruth St. Denis and Ted Shawn. In 1919 she made her solo debut with the Denishawn Company as the female lead in Shawn's ballet with an Aztec theme, *Xochitl.* Four years later Miss Graham left Denishawn and was for a while a solo dancer with the *Greenwich Village Follies* and a member of the dance faculty at the Eastman School of Music. On 18 April 1926 she appeared at the 48th Street Theatre in New York in a program of eighteen of her own choreographed works. A new era in American modern dance history was begun. Her first works reflected her Denishawn training, but later she broke with all the old traditions to create her own easily identifiable style. All the traditional steps and movements of classical ballet went out the window as Miss Graham evolved a new language of dance movement. She chose at times to work on a bare stage with only costumes and lights. She is credited as being the first of our time to use movable scenery, speech with dancing, and a chorus commenting upon the dance in progress. On 9 January 1930 the *New York Times* carried a headline "MARTHA GRAHAM GIVES DANCE WITHOUT MUSIC" when she introduced her *Project in Movement for a Divine Comedy* during a program at Maxine Elliot's Theatre. Since 1926 Martha Graham has created well over one hundred dances. Some, such as *Lamentation,* which she first danced on 8 January 1930 in a seamless tubelike costume of knitted wool and seated on a bench, and *Imperial Gesture,* were commentary on human experience. Others, such as *El Penitente,* created in August 1940 at the Bennington Dance Festival, of which Miss Graham was a founder, and *Appalachian Spring,* which Miss Graham first danced in the Coolidge Auditorium of The Library of Congress on 30 October 1944, were derived from American themes. Still others, *Errand into the Maze, Clytemnestra, Alcestis,* and *Phaedra,* are obviously dancings of classical tales. In staging her creations she has collaborated with numerous notable contemporary composers, including Samuel Barber, Paul Hindemith, Gian-Carlo Menotti, Aaron Copland, and Norman Dello Joio. Isamu Noguchi has been the designer of handsome sets and costumes for her productions, notably, *Frontier,* 1935; *Appalachian Spring,* 1944; *Night Journey,* 1947; *Embattled Garden,* 1958; and *Phaedra,* 1962. In 1962 Martha Graham and her company appeared in Israel on a tour sponsored by the State Department Cultural Exchange Program. For Tel-Aviv, Miss Graham created her work *Legend of Judith* which she first danced there in the Habima Theatre 25 October 1962. Since 1927 Miss Graham has been the head of the Martha Graham School of Contemporary Dance in New York and at present teaches also in the summer at Connecticut College. Although she now seldom appears on stage she remains a principal force in contemporary dance.

63. Martha Graham
by Isamu Noguchi, 1928
Bronze, 14 inches high
Lent by Honolulu Academy of Arts

Angna Enters
1907–

Outside of the silent cinema, there have been few American mimes of note in our century. The best known, undoubtedly, is Angna Enters. Born in New York on 28 April 1907, Miss Enters made her stage debut in her home town at the Greenwich Village Theatre in the spring of 1924. The production was a program of dance and mime entitled *Compositions in Dance Form,* in which she not only starred, but for which she had also designed the sets and costumes. With her program retitled *The Theatre of Angna Enters,* she began, several years later, to make annual tours of North America. Miss Enters has been credited with coining the term "dance mime" to describe her unique contribution to the performing arts, and in this subtle media she created, since her first performances in Greenwich Village, about 160 separate episodes and compositions. She has gotten her inspiration from many sources. There has been a series of compositions based on readings from Proust, one was inspired by the paintings of the eighteenth-century French artist Chardin, and others were based on individual and distinctive characters, such as her "Boy Cardinal" and "Queen of Heaven." On 25 January 1943 Angna Enters became the first person ever to stage a theatrical entertainment in New York's Metropolitan Museum of Art. Her work was entitled *Pagan Greece,* and for it she not only designed and executed her own costumes and choreography, but she composed the music and played all of the roles—some one dozen in number. In 1952, while touring in England, she played two weeks of repertory at the Mercury Theatre, performed at Cambridge University, and was honored as the subject of a special program on BBC TV. Whitney Bolton in the *New York Morning Telegraph* of 4 March 1959 penned as complimentary a description of a performer as any critic when he wrote, "Angna Enters is not solely a mime, nor distinctly an actress, nor uniquely a dancer. Her public performances combine all of these into an Enteresque concept no Counterfeiter ever has been able to equal." Miss Enters' paintings have been widely exhibited since her first one woman exhibition in New York in 1933, and in October of 1963 a showing of her original designs for sets and costumes was a feature of the International Theatre Exhibition at Naples, Italy.

64. Angna Enters
by Isamu Noguchi, 1931
Bronze, 11¼ inches high
Lent by Metropolitan Museum of Art

Josef Casimir Hofmann
1876-1957

"A thunder of applause swept through the house. Many people leaped to their feet. Men shouted 'Bravo!' and women waved their handkerchiefs. Pianists of repute were moved almost to tears. Some wiped the moisture from their eyes." The critic was W. J. Henderson of the *New York Times* and the occasion, the American debut at the Metropolitan Opera House, 29 November 1887, of the eleven-year-old Polish pianist Josef Casimir Hofmann. Born in Cracow on 20 January 1876 of musical parents, he had as early as age seven played the first movement of the Beethoven first piano concerto in public concert. Josef had already toured in Germany, Scandinavia, and Holland before coming to America. His announced tour of eighty performances here was cut short when the Society for the Prevention of Cruelty to Children protested the exploitation of one so young, and he was taken back to Europe. There further studies ensued, and eventually, when he was sixteen, he became a pupil of Anton Rubinstein. He appeared again in the United States in 1898 a fully matured artist, many of his critics conceding that no pianist since his venerable teacher had exhibited such consummate command of his instrument. Under the pseudonym Michel Dvorsky he also wrote for the piano. In 1922 he revealed himself as the true composer of the new works he had been introducing, and on 2 January 1924 the Philadelphia Orchestra devoted an entire concert to pieces by Josef Hofmann, alias Michel Dvorsky. From 1927 until 1938, when he resigned so that he could again devote his time to concertizing and composing, he was director of the Curtis Institute of Music in Philadelphia. It was a festive occasion at the Metropolitan Opera House on 28 November 1937 when he gave a golden-jubilee concert celebrating his debut as a child prodigy fifty years before. Well-wishers in the audience included Fiorello La Guardia, Walter Damrosch, and the Ambassador of Poland. The President of the United States sent his congratulations. Perhaps the finest salute came from the reviewer in the *New York Times* on the following day who described his entrance onstage, "This was an artist, simple and modest and sincere, about to sit before his instrument and make music." Hofmann died in Los Angeles on 16 February 1957.

65. Josef Hofmann at Carnegie Hall
by Charles E. Chambers, not dated
Oil on canvas, 30 x 30
Lent by Steinway & Sons

Fritz Kreisler
1875-1962

Born in Vienna on 2 February 1875, Fritz Kreisler graduated from the Vienna Conservatory at age ten and four years later made his first concert tour of the United States in the company of the pianist Moritz Rosenthal. Their first concert was played in Boston on 9 November 1888. Returning to Europe, Kreisler temporarily gave up his music for the study of medicine in Vienna, art in Paris, and a commission in an Austrian army regiment. Resigning his commission after about a year in uniform, he returned to the study of the violin. His debut as a violin soloist took place in Berlin in the spring of 1899. Tours of the United States followed between 1901 and 1903, and it was here that he was first acclaimed as a great violinist. Recalled into the Austrian army with the advent of World War I, Fritz Kreisler's second tour of military duty was of very short duration. Three months after his call he was wounded and discharged. He returned to the United States to raise money for his native country through his playing. When the United States entered the war against Austria, he retired from the concert stage but remained in this country. His return to the concert stage in New York in 1919 was the cause of great joy among his following. His playing was at its finest at about this time, and much of his music was preserved on phonograph records; between 1916 and 1946 he made over 200. On records and in his concerts he frequently played little pieces which he announced as transcriptions of works by the master composers of the eighteenth and nineteenth centuries. In 1935 he brought down on himself the scorn and condemnation of many critics when he announced that he had written most of the compositions. His public, not being as narrow-minded as the professional critics, saw this revelation as insufficient reason to desert their favorite. The audiences that filled every concert hall where he appeared zealously applauded both his lilting virtuoso technique and the delightful short compositions which one of the kinder critics called "transfigured salon music." Fritz Kreisler became a French citizen in 1938 when Germany annexed Austria. When the Nazi army invaded France he came permanently to this country and became an American citizen in 1943. He retired from the concert stage in 1950 and died in New York on 29 January 1962.

66. Fritz Kreisler
by Boris Chaliapin, 1943
Gouache and pencil on paper, 22 x 30
Lent by the Artist

His public singing career began during his student days, at Sligo College, and in 1904 John McCormack won a gold medal at the National Irish Festival in Dublin. Shortly afterward, he appeared in America for the first time on a short concert tour. Returning to Europe, he went to Italy for serious study and made his debut in opera in Savona in Pietro Mascagni's *L'Amico Fritz* in December of 1905. Neither Ireland nor England took notice of him until he appeared on 1 March 1907 at one of the Queen's Hall ballad concerts arranged by the London publisher Arthur Boosey. The result of this and subsequent concerts was his debut at Covent Gardens on 15 October 1907 as Turridu in Mascagni's *Cavalleria rusticana*. Later in the same season he appeared in Verdi's *Rigoletto* and Mozart's *Don Giovanni*. On 10 November 1909 John McCormack made his American operatic debut at Oscar Hammerstein's Manhattan Opera House singing Alfredo in Verdi's *La Traviata*. From that time on McCormack was a conspicuous and beloved part of the American musical scene. He became a member of the Boston Opera Company in 1910, and from 1912 to 1914 he sang in opera in Philadelphia and Chicago. He also made several appearances at the Metropolitan Opera and began his long and fantastically successful career on the American concert stage. Rather light voiced for opera, it was as a recitalist that John McCormack really excelled. In 1917 Olin Downes wrote of his concert singing; "his mastery included the clear enunciation of the English language, and the making of this tongue beautiful in song." During World War I he devoted much of his time to recitals to raise money for wartime charities and for Liberty Bond sales, and in 1919 he became a citizen of the United States, the country that had done so much to further his career. In concert he always sang to a sold-out house; his sale of phonograph records was second only to Caruso's. McCormack himself considered his recording of "Il mio tesoro" from *Don Giovanni* his finest effort for the phonograph. A new song was insured success if it appeared on a McCormack program. His recital repertory was light on operatic selections and consisted primarily of the classic airs of oratorio, of lieder, and of Irish songs, sung in so masterful a manner as to elevate them above the realm of the simple and popular. Like his friend Fritz Kreisler, he was accused by some critics of cheapening his music with light music. John McCormack, however, appreciated the adulation of his public and went on giving them what they wanted and enjoyed. Except for a slight period of inactivity in 1922, due to illness, his concert tours continued until his retirement in 1937. He returned to his native country, Ireland, and lived there until his death on 16 September 1945.

67. John McCormack
by Sir William Orpen, 1923
Oil on canvas, 41 x 34
Lent by Count Cyril McCormack

Born in London, Gertrude Lawrence first appeared on stage in her native country at age nine as a dancer in a pantomime. She was first seen in the United States in New York when she came here with an *Andrè Charlot's Revue* in 1924. She achieved her first notable Broadway success as the Kay of George and Ira Gershwin's *Oh Kay!* when it premiered at the Imperial Theatre in November of 1926. In 1928 she appeared with Clifton Webb in *Treasure Girl,* one of few Gershwin failures. As her star brightened over Broadway she received critical acclaim for her appearances with Noel Coward in both *Private Lives,* which opened at the Times Square Theatre on 27 January 1931, and for *Tonight at 8:30,* one of the hits of the fabulous New York theater season of 1936–1937. In October of 1937 she began a long run in the role of Susan Trexel in Rachel Crother's *Susan and God* and was so successful in her part that one of New York's evangelists invited her to recite one of the play's more fervently religious speeches from his pulpit. Two seasons later she had another hit when she created the role of Lydia Kenyon in Sampson Raphaelson's *The Skylark,* which opened at the Morosco Theatre on 11 October 1939. On 23 January 1941 she created the role of Liza Elliott in Kurt Weill's *Lady in the Dark* when it began its run at the Alvin Theatre. Challenged by the immediate success of comedian Danny Kaye, making his Broadway debut with her in this show, she gave what one of her critics termed, "one of the remarkable virtuoso performances of our contemporary musical stage." In December of 1945 she opened in New Haven in a revival of Shaw's *Pygmalion* which went on to a very successful New York engagement and a coast-to-coast tour. She saw in Anna Leonowens, the main character in Margaret Landon's novel *Anna and the King of Siam,* a superb vehicle for herself and persuaded Richard Rodgers and Oscar Hammerstein II to prepare a musical version for the New York stage. The result, *The King and I,* opened at the St. James Theatre on 29 March 1951 to critical acclaim. With Yul Brenner as her King of Siam, Gertrude Lawrence gave resplendent performances as Anna, English tutor to the king's children, until three weeks before her death on 6 September 1952. At curtain time on the evening of the day of her funeral the lights on the marquees of the theater districts in both New York and London were blacked out for two minutes in tribute to the departed star.

68. Gertrude Lawrence
by Ben Ali Haggin, 1931
Pastel on paper, 50 x 36
Lent by Museum of the City of New York,
Theatre and Music Collection

A relative of the famed British acting family, the Terrys, John Gielgud first appeared on stage as the Herald in Shakespeare's *Henry V* at London's Old Vic in November of 1921. His first appearance in the United States was at New York's Majestic Theatre on 19 January 1928 as the Grand Duke Alexander in *The Patriot*. It was a minor role and the play lasted only twelve performances. Returning to London, John Gielgud's reputation grew with his successive appearances on the stages of that city, and particularly with his own production of *Hamlet* in 1934 in which he took the title role. The production ran for 185 performances, a London theater record surpassed only by Sir Henry Irving's production of sixty years before. In 1936 Gielgud returned to New York with his *Hamlet* and opened at the Empire Theatre on 8 October. Judith Anderson was his Queen and Lillian Gish was his Ophelia in a production that most of the critics accepted as the outstanding *Hamlet* of their time. Brooks Atkinson, writing in the *New York Times* on 18 October, went so far in his enthusiasm as to give John Gielgud the power of posthumous mindreading when he said, Gielgud "has not only the youth but also the temperament to understand Hamlet as Shakespeare imagined him." John Anderson, in the *Evening Journal,* writing perhaps with unconscious chauvinism, found Gielgud's melancholy Dane second to that of John Barrymore, but admitted that some of his quieter passages were "nothing short of perfection." John Gielgud's *Hamlet* ran for 132 performances, thirty-two more than that of Barrymore in 1922. After World War II, Gielgud was much in evidence on the American stage. In the Spring of 1947 alone, he appeared in New York in productions of Oscar Wilde's *The Importance of Being Ernest,* Congreve's *Love for Love,* and Robinson Jeffers' adaptation of *Medea* playing Jason opposite Judith Anderson in the title role. Late in December he opened at the National Theatre as Raskolnikoff in Rodney Ackland's version of Dostoevsky's *Crime and Punishment.* Brooks Atkinson considered Gielgud's characterization in this role as one of his masterpieces. In 1950 he reappeared as Thomas Mendip in Christopher Fry's *The Lady's Not for Burning.* In acknowledgment of his services to the British stage, knighthood was conferred upon him by Queen Elizabeth II in the Coronation and Birthday Honors of 1953, and he became Sir John Gielgud. In 1958 he toured Canada and the United States with *The Ages of Man* and then opened in New York with his montage of Shakespearean passages at the 46th Street Theatre on 18 December. After a lengthy tour with the same production which took him as far afield as Australia and New Zealand, Sir John opened with it again in New York in April of 1963. He was last seen on the New York stage during the season of 1970–1971 as one of the four-person cast of David Storey's *Home.*

69. Sir John Gielgud in the title role of Shakespeare's *Hamlet*
by Richmond Barthé, circa 1936
Bronze, 20 inches high
Lent by American Shakespeare Festival Theatre

Maurice Evans
1901-

Nine years after his professional debut at the Festival Theatre in Cambridge, England, in 1926, Maurice Evans first appeared on Broadway as Romeo to Katharine Cornell's Juliet. Two years and three months later he opened at the St. James Theatre in the title role of Shakespeare's *Richard II*. It was the first time New York had seen the play since Edwin Booth had acted it in 1875. Brooks Atkinson in his *New York Times* column of 6 February 1937 wrote, "Maurice Evans now deserves a sort of reverence for his triumphant performance as Richard II." Richard Lockridge in the *New York Sun* of the same date reported that Evans' reading of an important passage "brought applause such as used to greet actors when they made their 'points,' and Mr. Evans deserved it." Even Bosley Crowther who headed his *Times* column on 14 February with "HERE IS ONE OF THOSE ENGLISHMEN AGAIN" and decried that "Broadway has had its craw crammed with English actors this season" conceded that Evans had won the season's laurels with his portrayal of Richard II. It was an auspicious beginning to a long New York career which included his performances of *Hamlet* in 1939, Malvolio in *Twelfth Night* in 1940, and *Macbeth* in 1942. During World War II, Evans served in the United States Army in charge of Army Entertainment Section, Central Pacific Area. His abbreviated "G.I. version" of *Hamlet* toured for the troops and was seen in New York in 1945 and again in 1946. As a producer he is responsible for the musical *The Teahouse of the August Moon*, 1953, *No Time for Sergeants*, 1955, and he both produced and acted in *Heartbreak House* at the Billy Rose Theatre in 1959. In 1962 he played with Helen Hayes in a program of readings from Shakespeare, *A Program for Two Players*, which followed its successful premiere at the American Shakespeare Festival with a season-long, cross-country tour.

70. Maurice Evans in the title role of Shakespeare's *Richard II*
by Richmond Barthé, circa 1937
Bronze, 22 inches high
Lent by American Shakespeare Festival Theatre

Born in Copenhagen on 20 March 1890, Lauritz Melchior made his operatic debut as a baritone at the Royal Opera House in his native city on 2 April 1912. Convinced by colleagues that he was really a tenor he pursued further studies and made his second debut, again at the Royal Opera, on 8 October 1918 in Wagner's *Tannhäuser*. Concentrating on Wagnerian roles, he appeared for the first time as Siegmund in London's Covent Garden in May of 1924 and two months later in the title role in *Parsifal* at Bayreuth. It was as Tannhäuser that he sang for the first time at the Metropolitan Opera House during a matinee performance on 17 February 1926. His debut was overshadowed by the excitement attending the debut that night of an American soprano, and he was coolly received. One critic found his voice "forced and rough." As he became more comfortable on the stage of the Met, however, it became slowly obvious to all who heard him that he was the "heldentenor" the New York company had been seeking for years. Wagner again received his due in New York, and it was Melchior's prerogative to be leading man to the principal Wagnerian sopranos of his time. On 16 January 1933 he was Tristan to Frida Leider's Isolde at the latter's Metropolitan debut. He assisted Lotte Lehmann at her debut on 11 January 1934 in *Die Walküre*—he was Siegmund to her Sieglinde—and on 28 December 1939 played the same unknowingly incestuous sibling at Helen Traubel's debut. The Norwegian soprano Kirsten Flagstad sang for the first time at the Metropolitan on 2 February 1935 and three days later Lauritz Melchior sang *Tristan und Isolde* with her for the first time. With these two stalwart singers in the roles of the unhappy lovers the Wagner opus assumed unprecedented popularity on Broadway. In a review, dated 23 December 1936, W. J. Henderson called Melchior's Tristan "the best the Metropolitan had known since Jean de Reszke." There could hardly be higher praise. Melchior's two-hundredth performance of the role occurred on the Met stage on 4 December 1944, and in 1946 he celebrated twenty years with the company by singing a gala Sunday concert on the anniversary date of his debut. The proceeds he donated to a fund for a new production of Wagner's *Ring* cycle. His last appearance at the Metropolitan was as Lohengrin on 2 February 1950. Although he had retired from the operatic stage, his career had not ended. He appeared frequently in concert, on television, and following the example of one of his leading ladies, in nightclubs. His singing roles in motion pictures have brought opera to many who otherwise might never have discovered it.

71. Lauritz Melchior as Tristan in Richard Wagner's *Tristan und Isolde*
by Nickol Schattenstein, 1937
Oil on canvas, 50 x 42
Lent by Betty Smith Associates

5828-R

Nikol.
Schattenstein

Dorothy Stickney
1900–

In the summer of 1921, just after graduation from the Northwestern Dramatic School in Minneapolis, Dorothy Stickney made her stage debut with a quartet called the "Southern Belles." Her New York stage debut came when she opened in *The Squall*. The play was short lived, and on 30 December she opened at the Music Box as Liz in Maurine Watkins' melodrama about the travesty of justice, *Chicago*. After a reprise which included some gentle acting in a revival of *The Beaux Stratagem,* another juicy role as a big-city hussy came her way when she opened in the late summer of 1928 as Mollie Molloy in Charles MacArthur and Ben Hecht's *The Front Page*. Eleven years and a half-dozen roles later, Dorothy Stickney created the role which will always be re-membered as her greatest contribution to the New York stage—Vinnie in *Life with Father*. Adapted by her husband, Howard Lindsay, and Russel Crouse from the book by Clarence Day, the play costarring Howard Lindsay as Father opened at the Empire Theatre on 8 November 1939 for a recored-making run of 3,224 performances. Brooks Atkinson, in his *New York Times* review the following day, called it "a perfect comedy" and an "authentic part of our American folklore." Walter Winchell, in the *New York Daily Mirror* of the same date, complimented three noted comediennes when he wrote, "Dorothy Stickney, essays the role of Mrs. Day as Billie Burke and Gracie Allen would toy with it. This combination, you can easily imagine, makes for hilarious amusement." So sympathetic was Dorothy Stickney's playing of Vinnie that the same authors wrote a sequel, *Life with Mother*, which opened at the Empire on 20 October 1948. Again starring Howard Lindsay and Dorothy Stickney in their original characters of Mr. and Mrs. Day, Brooks Atkinson found the sequel in some respects "more beguiling" than the original. But during the Second World War, American tastes had changed, and *Life with Mother* had a relatively short run of 265 performances. Dorothy Stickney played a series of roles on Broadway between 1951 and 1955 and then opened in Abingdon, Virginia's Barter Theatre in September of 1958 in a one-woman show entitled *A Lovely Light*. In February of 1960 she played it in New York's Hudson Theatre and then took it to London for an engagement at the Globe late that spring. From 1960 until 1962 she toured the United States with *A Lovely Light* and then reopened in New York at the Mayfair Theatre on 6 January 1964. Miss Stickney was last seen on Broadway during the season of 1970–1971 in Brian Freel's *Monday Scheme*.

72. Dorothy Stickney as Vinnie in Howard Lindsay and
Russel Crouse's *Life with Father*
by John Falter, circa 1940
Oil on canvas, 46 x 34
Lent by Dorothy Stickney

Alicia Markova
1910-

By the time Alicia Markova made her dance debut in the United States in the autumn of 1938 she had been onstage for fourteen years and had secured an enviable reputation in her native England. She had been accepted in the Diaghilev Ballets Russes at age fourteen and had remained with that company until Serge Diaghilev's death in 1929. With that company she created the title role in George Balanchine's *Le Rossignol* in 1926. Moving on to London's Ballet Rambert she created leading roles in *La Péri, Les Masques,* and *Mephisto Valse,* all choreographed by Frederick Ashton. In April of 1931 she also created the Polka in Ashton's *Façade,* which he choreographed to music by William Walton. In 1933 she became the first prima ballerina of the Vic-Wells (now Royal) Ballet. While with that company she became the first English ballerina to dance the title role in *Giselle* and the dual roles of Odette and Odile in a full-length production of Peter Tchaikovsky's *Swan Lake.* With Anton Dolin she organized the Markova-Dolin Company and danced as its prima ballerina from 1935 until 1938. In that year she became a ballerina in the René Blum-Leonide Massine Ballet Russe de Monte Carlo. When she danced the title role in *Giselle* in the company's first New York season in 1938 she became an immediate favorite of and influence on American audiences. She was a ballerina with the Ballet (now American Ballet) Theatre from 1941 until 1944 and again in the season of 1945-1946. For the Ballet Theatre she created the important role of Juliet in Antony Tudor's *Romeo and Juliet* set to music of Frederick Delius. The ballet, with decor by Eugene Berman, was premiered at the Metropolitan Opera House in New York on 6 April 1943 in unfinished form and four days later was given in full. In the season of 1945-1946 Miss Markova formed a new Markova-Dolin Company and took it on tour of the United States. In the spring and summer of 1947 her company toured in Mexico and Central America. In 1948 she toured the Philippines with Anton Dolin and the following year South Africa. Returning to London, Alicia Markova was co-founder with Anton Dolin of the London Festival Ballet in 1950-1951 and its prima ballerina. After twelve years as guest dancer with leading companies all over the world, Miss Markova danced for the last time with the London Festival Ballet in 1962. She announced her retirement on 1 January 1963 and three months later became director of the Metropolitan Opera Ballet. Her influence in the old yellow-brick opera house on Broadway was not slight. On 15 November 1964 she presented the Metropolitan Opera Ballet in *Les Sylphides* and as a result of its successful reception by the administration and public, a ballet evening was scheduled at the opera house for 11 April 1965. It was only the second time in the eighty-year history of the Opera that such an evening had been scheduled. Of more widespread influence was certainly Miss Markova's direction of the Metropolitan Ballet Studio which performed before thousands of public school children in New York. For her importance in ballet in Great Britain she was made a Commander of the Order of the British Empire in 1960 and a Dame of the Order of the British Empire in 1963. She is at present Distinguished Guest Lecturer on Ballet with the College-Conservatory of Music of the University of Cincinnati.

73. Dame Alicia Markova as Odette in Tchaikovsky's ballet *Swan Lake*
by Boris Chaliapin, 1941
Gouache on paper, 60 x 33

Lent by the Artist

Lucia Chase
1907-

After graduation from St. Margaret's Academy in her native Waterbury, Connecticut, Lucia Chase studied acting at the Theatre Guild School and dancing with several of the leading names in twentieth century ballet and choreography, Mikhail Mordkin, Michel Fokine, Antony Tudor, Bronislava Nijinska, and others. In 1938 and 1939 she was a ballerina with the newly organized Mordkin Ballet. Miss Chase danced in *Giselle, La Fille Mal Gardée, The Goldfish,* and various other works under Mordkin's direction. In the autumn of 1939 the Mordkin Ballet became Ballet Theatre with Lucia Chase as founder-director. With her company she created a number of notable dance roles. She was Minerva when the Antony Tudor ballet *Judgment of Paris,* set to music from Kurt Weill's *The Three Penny Opera,* was first danced at New York's Center Theatre on 23 January 1940; she was The Greedy One at the premiere performance of Agnes de Mille's *Three Virgins and a Devil* on 11 February 1941. Later the same year, on 12 November, she danced Floretta in the American premiere of Fokine's *Bluebeard* in the Forty-fourth Street Theatre, New York. When the Antony Tudor choreographed *Pillar of Fire,* set to the music of Arnold Schönberg's *Verklärte Nacht,* was premiered by Ballet Theatre at the Metropolitan Opera House on 8 April 1942, Lucia Chase created the role of the Oldest Sister; on 29 November 1942 she was the first Pallas Athena in David Lachine's *Helen of Troy* at its premiere performance in Detroit by the touring company. The following spring, on 6 April, Lucia Chase created the role of the Nurse in Antony Tudor's *Romeo and Juliet.* Although she did not create the role of the Stepmother in *Fall River Legend,* the ballet made from the story of Lizzi Borden to music by Morton Gould and choreographed by Agnes de Mille, Miss Chase danced the role with her company for ten years. In 1945 Ballet Theatre became the American Ballet Theatre and Lucia Chase became codirector with Oliver Smith. Under their directorship the company has become one of the leading dance organizations in the United States. From August through December of 1950 the company, traveling as the American National Ballet Theatre, made its first European tour under the auspices of the State Department. Other foreign tours followed, the most notable being the September 1960 tour by which American Ballet Theatre became the first American dance company to appear in the Soviet Union. The American Ballet Theatre has been named a resident company of The John F. Kennedy Center for the Performing Arts.

74. Lucia Chase in the ballet *Capriccioso*
by Boris Chaliapin, 1941
Gouache on paper, 60 x 33
Lent by the Artist

Paul Robeson
1898-

A native of New Jersey, Paul Robeson was born in Princeton on 9 April 1898 and educated at Rutgers College, where he was selected twice as an All-American football player, and at Columbia University. He made his New York acting debut in *Simon the Cyrenian* at the Lafayette Theatre in 1921 and subsequently appeared as Jim in *Taboo* in New York and Blackpool, England. He was the personal choice of the playwright to be Brutus Jones in Eugene O'Neill's *The Emperor Jones* at Provincetown Playhouse, in short runs during May and December of 1924. London playgoers saw him in the part when he opened at the Ambassadors' Theatre in the English capital in early autumn of 1925. His first appearances in the musical theater came when he essayed the roles of Crown in Gershwin's *Porgy and Bess* in 1927 and Joe in Jerome Kern's *Show Boat* in London in 1928. During the 1929-1930 season he sang a number of concerts throughout Europe and also appeared in *The Emperor Jones* in Berlin. Robeson played Othello for the first time at London's Savoy Theatre on 19 May 1930. In 1936, again in London, he created the role of the liberator of Haiti on C. L. R. James' play *Toussaint l'Ouverture*. It opened at the Westminster Theatre in March, and London critics found Mr. Robeson's characterization both sympathetic and important to the vitality of the play. Recognizing Paul Robeson's individuality as an artist, Charles Darwin, in *The Times* of 22 March 1936, wrote that, "his appearance and voice entitle him to rules of his own." He returned to the New York stage in the title role of *John Henry,* opening at the 44th Street Theatre on 10 January 1940. As a recitalist on the concert stage, he enjoyed phenomenal success. One concert in Chicago's Grant Park was attended by an estimated 150,000 persons. On 19 October 1943 he played Othello for the first time in his native country in a Theatre Guild production at the Schubert Theatre. His Desdemona was Uta Hagen and his Iago, José Ferrer. The criticism of Mr. Robeson's acting was buried under the controversy caused by the loud cries from the more than mildly racist critics, who found a real black man in the role of Othello offensive. The play ran, however, for 280 performances on Broadway—a record for a Shakespearean production—and later toured. During his travels in Europe, Paul Robeson had become more and more sympathetic to the aims and aspirations of the Soviet Union and, during a period of near hysterical anti-Communist feeling in the United States, was denied his passport in August of 1950. His professional activities were curtailed by his inability to travel abroad and by the inaccessibility of concert halls in this country. In 1958 he returned to Europe where he was named an honorary professor at the Moscow State Conservatory of Music and where he played the title role in *Othello* at the Shakespeare Memorial Theatre, Stratford-upon-Avon, on 7 April 1959. He did not return to the United States until 1964—then to retirement in Philadelphia.

75. Paul Robeson in the title role of Shakespeare's *Othello*
by Betsy Graves Reyneau, circa 1943
Oil on canvas, 50¼ x 38
From the collection of the National Portrait Gallery

As early as 1920 the newspapers of her native Philadelphia took notice of Marian Anderson when she assisted the tenor Roland Hayes in concert: "Marian Anderson also sang, and made a profound impression." A relatively short time later as careers go, on 26 August 1925, she sang a successful concert at Lewisohn Stadium in New York and then left for further study in Europe. As with so many other young American artists it was there where she first won fame. During a 1931 concert tour of Scandinavia she sang for Jan Sibelius who honored her by dedicating his song "Solitude" to her. She was offered the title role in George Bizet's *Carmen* by Konstantin Stanislavski after he heard her sing in Moscow. Would she have declined that honor if she had known it would be at least twenty years before she was to appear in opera? Her voice and her artistry matured and, shortly before returning home late in 1935, she sang at the Salzburg Festival. After the concert Arturo Toscanini assured her, "Yours is a voice one hears once in a hundred years." All her reviews from that time on were to echo that praise. Howard Taubman in the *New York Times* said of her 30 December 1935 Town Hall recital, "Marian Anderson has returned to her native land one of the great singers of our time. . . ." In Europe again, a concert at the Paris Opéra was a complete sellout. Only Rachmaninoff and Fritz Kreisler had accomplished this before her. In 1936 the Roosevelts invited her to sing in their private quarters at the White House. Three years later and only three blocks from the White House she was denied the use of Constitution Hall because she was black. After the District of Columbia Board of Education also denied her the use of the auditorium at Central High School, she was invited to sing an outdoor concert. For many of her admirers her most noble moment was that Easter Sunday 1939 when she sang from the steps of the Lincoln Memorial. In 1943 a mural of that emotional event was dedicated nearby in the Department of the Interior building. Emotional also was her debut, too late in her career, at the Metropolitan Opera House on 7 January 1955. The *New York Times* noted that "men as well as women in the audience were dabbing at their eyes." She was the first black singer to appear as a featured performer with the resident company on that stage in the seventy-two years of its history. Her expressive voice and her character had made her beloved around the world. In 1957, during a tour of Asia sponsored by the State Department, she became the first foreigner ever to be invited to speak at the Mahatma Gandhi memorial in Delhi. In July 1958 she was appointed a member of the United States Delegation to the United Nations by President Dwight D. Eisenhower. It was an honor that befitted her nation's regard for her artistry. She was elected to the American Academy of Arts and Sciences the following year, and on 6 December 1963 she became one of the first recipients of the Presidential Medal of Freedom. Her citation read in part: "Marian Anderson, artist and citizen . . . she has ennobled her race and her country, while her voice has enthralled the world." Her official farewell concert was sung at Carnegie Hall on 19 April 1965.

76. Marian Anderson
by Betsy Graves Reyneau, circa 1943
Oil on canvas, 60 x 38
From the collection of the National Portrait Gallery

Ethel Merman
1909-

A native of Long Island, Ethel Merman began her show business career in New York nightclubs and in vaudeville. One of her first engagements was at the Palace Theatre in the autumn of 1929 with a group that included Jimmy Durante. Her first appearance in a musical was as Kate Fothergill in George and Ira Gershwin's *Girl Crazy* which opened at the Alvin Theatre on 14 October 1930. Her trumpet-voice renditions stopped the show and put her solidly in the theatrical headlines for the first time. When she sang her second feature number, "I Got Rhythm," a roaring audience demanded, and got, four encores. For that milestone performance George Gershwin himself conducted the orchestra which included as instrumentalists Benny Goodman and Glenn Miller. Not content with her vocal workout on the stage of the Alvin, Ethel Merman adjourned to the Central Park Casino every night after the closing of *Girl Crazy* to sing a late night show for its diamond-studded patronage. The following year found her opening at the Apollo Theatre on 14 September in *George White's Scandals* and then returning for a short while to vaudeville. Her next show, titled *Humpty Dumpty* when it flopped in Pittsburgh, was reworked into *Take a Chance* by its authors and made it to the Apollo by 26 November 1932, where it was a hit. Ethel Merman as Wanda Brill played with *Take a Chance* in both its New York and Chicago runs. More roles which Miss Merman herself called "hard-boiled Tessie type" followed between 1934 and 1943 when she created Reno Sweeney in *Anything Goes,* "Nails" O'Reilly Duquesne in Cole Porter's *Red, Hot and Blue,* Jeanette Adair in *Stars in Your Eyes,* Hattie Malony in *Panama Hattie,* and Blossom Hart in *Something for the Boys.* In February of 1946 she went into rehearsal for the role which helped her break away into a new mood—Annie Oakley. *Annie Get Your Gun* with music and lyrics by Irving Berlin, opened at the Imperial Theatre on 16 May 1946 after tryouts in New Haven, Boston, and Philadelphia. By New York opening night there was little doubt that Ethel Merman had created a role that would remain a classic in the annals of the American musical theater. *Annie Get Your Gun* graced the boards of the Imperial for 144 weeks. On 12 October 1950 she opened again at the Imperial in another Irving Berlin show, *Call Me Madam.* In the role of Sally Adams, lady ambassador, New York saw her for 644 performances; the rest of the country saw her when a motion picture version of the musical was released in 1953. In the same year she appeared with Mary Martin in the first two-hour television spectacular. December of 1956 saw her opening in *Happy Hunting,* a musical that had a healthy run of 412 performances, and on 21 May 1959 Ethel Merman opened at the Broadway Theatre in *Gypsy.* Spiced with her impersonation of Rose, a hardboiled stage mother, the show ran for 702 performances in New York and finally closed on a tour in St. Louis in December of 1961. In 1966, Ethel Merman again played Annie Oakley before sellout houses when *Annie Get Your Gun* was revived by the Music Theater of Lincoln Center. Ethel Merman was last seen on Broadway at the St. James Theatre when she assumed the role of Dolly Gallagher Levi in the record-setting Jerry Herman musical *Hello, Dolly!* The last in a series of singing actresses who had played the lead role since the show opened in January of 1964, Miss Merman was Dolly the night the show broke the record for longest running musical on Broadway and until its closing in December of 1970.

77. Ethel Merman as Annie Oakley in Irving Berlin's *Annie Get Your Gun*
by Rosemarie Sloat, 1971
Oil and acrylic on canvas, 84½ x 50
Lent by the Artist

Alfred Lunt
1892-

Lynn Fontanne
?-

Although Lynn Fontanne made her professional debut in a Christmas pantomime at London's Drury Lane Theatre on 26 December 1905 and Alfred Lunt made his at the Castle Square Theatre in Boston on 7 October 1912, the summer of 1919 is a more monumental calendar landmark for them. It was at this time in Washington, D.C., that they first acted together. As most American and English theatergoers know without being prompted, they have been together ever since. There are few times when one of them was a success in a production that did not also star the other. Alfred Lunt's portrayal of the title role in *Clarence* in 1919 and Miss Fontanne's achievements as Eliza Doolittle in the Theatre Guild production of Shaw's *Pygmalion* in 1926 are exceptions to the rule. They are the most famous dramatic duo in the history of theatricals in this country. A failure when is was first produced in New York, *The Guardsman* starring the Lunts was revived by the Theatre Guild in October of 1924 and became the first of that organization's productions to make money. From then on many of the Lunts' triumphs were to be in Guild productions, such as *The Goat Song,* 1926, *Elizabeth the Queen,* 1930, *Idiot's Delight,* 1936, and *Amphitryon 38,* 1937. In that same year, 1937, Alfred Lunt directed and they both starred in a Guild production of Shakespeare's *Taming of the Shrew*. It was a hit both in New York and on tour. Their appearance in Terence Rattigan's *O Mistress Mine* saved the Theatre Guild's 1945–1946 season from financial disaster. They had played it first in London under the title *Love in Idleness* and, after opening under the new title in New York on 23 January 1946, took it on to even further success on tour. Their performance as a team of mindreaders in *The Great Sebastians* was seen by millions when it went from stage to television production in 1957. On 5 May 1958 the Globe Theatre was reopened in New York as the Lunt-Fontanne Theatre with the titular saints of the building shining forth in the opening night production of Friedrich Dürrenmatt's *The Visit*. On 4 July 1964 they received jointly, as is only fitting and proper, the President's Medal of Freedom.

78. Alfred Lunt and Lynn Fontanne
by James Fosburgh, 1957
Oil on canvas, 59 x 39
Lent by Alfred Lunt

Benny Goodman
1909-

The eighth of eleven children of an immigrant tailor, Benny Goodman was born in Chicago 30 May 1909 and received his first clarinet and music lessons at the Kehelah Jacob Synagogue when he was ten. Other early musical training was received at the famous settlement house, Hull House, and he earned his first money as a musician when he was twelve. The following year he had his first union card, and at age fourteen he left school when he got a permanent job playing at Guyon's Paradise dance hall. From 1925 until 1929 Benny Goodman played with Ben Pollack's band in Los Angeles, and made his first recorded solo with Pollack in December of 1926. In 1929 he was in New York playing in the orchestra pit at musicals and on the dance floor at college proms. In March of 1934 he formed his own band and opened at Billy Rose's Music Hall. A cross-country tour in the winter of the 1934–1935 season was a failure until the band hit Los Angeles. When dancers stopped dancing and crowded around the bandstand to listen to the soloists the era of Swing had begun. In December of 1935 Benny Goodman held the first jazz concert in Chicago. Returning to New York more than 20,000 paid admission to hear his first concert in the Paramount Theatre in March of 1937, and Benny Goodman was declared "The King of Swing." On 16 January 1938 the walls of New York's prim and proper yellow-brick music hall on 57th Street echoed jazz for the first time when Benny Goodman performed a concert in Carnegie Hall. Shortly after the end of World War II, Benny Goodman broke up his band and did not assemble one again until early in 1956. In 1956 and 1957 he and his band made a most successful tour of Asia under the auspices of the Department of State, and in 1958 and 1959 he played at the Brussel's World's Fair and toured western Europe. On Benny Goodman's fifty-third birthday, in 1962, he and his band began a tour of thirty-two concerts in the Soviet Union. At home with the classics as well as jazz, Benny Goodman commissioned a work for clarinet and violin from the composer Béla Bartok and has played and recorded both Mozart's *Concerto in A for Clarinet* and the same composer's *Quintet in A for Clarinet and Strings*.

79. Benny Goodman
by René Bouché, 1960
Oil on canvas, 40 x 32
Lent by Benny Goodman

Arthur Rubinstein
1886-

Arthur Rubinstein began to study piano in his birthplace of Lodz, Poland, when he was three years old. Already at age four and again at age six he performed in public at charity concerts. After serious study in Warsaw and Berlin, he made his professional debut in the German capital at age twelve. Appearances in other German cities followed and he studied in Switzerland for a while with Paderewski. In January of 1906, Arthur Rubinstein made his American debut with the Philadelphia Orchestra playing the Frederic Chopin *Concerto in E-minor.* After an extended concert tour he returned to Europe for further study until he was satisfied that he had attained his maturity as an artist. Returning to the concert stage, he had completed a major tour of the European music centers when World War I began. He worked for a while in London as an interpreter for the Allied Forces and then embarked upon another tour with the noted violinist Eugene Ysaÿe. It was 1919 before he returned to the United States. His first concert of this second tour was played in New York's Carnegie Hall on 20 February 1919. New York was indeed impressed with his maturity, and one of the critics wrote that in his technique he had "traits sufficient to equip a half dozen artists." For about ten years Arthur Rubinstein was a frequent guest artist at American concerts. Then, for about another decade, he did not play in this country again until 21 November 1937 when he appeared as soloist with the New York Philharmonic. The major piece of that concert was the Tchaikovsky piano concerto and Olin Dowes wrote in his review that "the performance was distinguished by qualities of a brilliant pianist. . . ." Since that time Arthur Rubinstein has been a major figure in the history of concertizing and recording in the United States and, indeed, in the rest of the world. His preeminence in his profession has been honored officially by at least six nations, and his recordings are always the classical "best sellers." Selected for special praise by his critics is his playing of the works of Brahms, Chopin, and the Spanish composers De Falla and Granados. In 1932 Rubinstein had moved from his native Poland to Paris, and when World War II began he moved to the United States. He is currently "at home" in both New York and Paris. On 27 January 1971, the eve of his eighty-fourth birthday, Arthur Rubinstein played a concert in New York's Philharmonic Hall. As is usual when he appears now, the stage as well as the auditorium proper was filled with sold-out seats. The program included Liszt, Schubert, Schumann, Brahms, and Ravel. Raymond Ericson, reviewing the concert in the *New York Times* two days later, expressed what must have been the thoughts of most of his adoring audience on that occasion when he wrote, "the listener could only conclude that the great pianist was growing young magnificently" rather than growing old.

80. Arthur Rubinstein
by Nathan Rappoport, not dated
Bronze, 13 ⅛ inches high
Lent by Arthur Rubinstein

Leonard Bernstein's career as a composer and conductor began in earnest during his undergraduate years at Harvard. He conducted an orchestra for the first time there—the composition, his own incidental music to Aristophanes' *The Birds*—and he produced and directed a performance of Marc Blitzstein's *The Cradle Will Rock* at the university shortly after its controversial New York premiere. After graduate study at the Curtis Institute he became assistant to Serge Koussevitsky at the Tanglewood summer music festival. A long association with the New York Philharmonic began when he became, for one year, assistant to its director, Arthur Rodzinski, in 1934 and 1944. He conducted that orchestra for the first time in Carnegie Hall on 13 November 1943. So enthusiastic was his reception by audience and press that within one year he traveled 50,000 miles and appeared at 100 concerts as guest conductor. In January of 1944 his *Jeremiah Symphony* was heard for the first time and won the New York Critics' Award as "outstanding orchestral work by an American composer" introduced during that season. Bernstein's fame as a composer was enhanced by his music for the ballet *Fancy Free* written for the Ballet Theatre and danced for the first time by that company at the Metropolitan Opera House on 18 April 1944. Choreographed by Jerome Robbins, it received an astounding 161 performances during its first season. With Adolph Green and Betty Comdon, Bernstein reworked the story line of *Fancy Free* into a full-blown musical which opened as *On the Town* at New York's Adelphi Theatre on 28 December 1944. After a successful Broadway run it was made into a motion picture and was revived in New York in two productions running simultaneously in 1959. In the autumn of 1945 Leonard Bernstein became director of the New York City Symphony and continued to make guest appearances in the United States and abroad. Notable were his appearances with the Palestine Symphony in 1947 and his conducting of *Medea* with Maria Callas at La Scala in 1953. He was the first native American ever to conduct during the regular season of that opera house. His opera, *Trouble in Tahiti,* premiered at the Festival of the Creative Arts at Brandeis University on 12 June 1952, was followed in February of 1953 with the first performances of the award-winning *Wonderful Town* which he wrote with Adolph Green and Betty Comdon. Leonard Bernstein's first television appearance on 14 November 1954 set a new style for symphonic lecturing and conducting in that medium. In 1956 his very operatic musical *Candide* opened at the Martin Beck Theatre in New York and closed much sooner than it deserved after seventy-three performances. His next attempt at the musical comedy idiom, however, *West Side Story,* opened on 26 September 1957 at the Winter Garden and became one of the great all-time successes on Broadway. After closing in New York it went on tour and then returned to New York for a second engagement. During the 1957–1958 season Leonard Bernstein was announced as successor to Dimitri Mitropoulos, Director of the New York Philharmonic. So successful were his innovations, such as cycles of concerts built around specific composers or themes, and his open rehearsals or "Preview Concerts," that the advance sale for the 1959–1960 season passed the one-million-dollar mark. In 1958 the New York Philharmonic made a 15,000 mile tour of Central and South America and the following

81. Leonard Bernstein
by René Bouché, 1960
Oil on canvas, 50 x 40
Lent by Leonard Bernstein

year toured Europe, the Near East, and countries behind the Iron Curtain. Everywhere Leonard Bernstein's conducting was most enthusiastically received. His reception in Russia was especially emotional. At the orchestra's last Russian concert in Moscow on 11 September 1959, Bernstein conducted Dimitri Shostakovich's *Fifth Symphony*. At its conclusion, the composer rushed to the stage to embrace Bernstein as the packed house gave them a standing ovation. On 23 September 1962 Leonard Bernstein conducted the New York Philharmonic for the first time in their new permanent home in New York's Lincoln Center. In March of 1964 he crossed the plaza at Lincoln Center to make his directorial debut at the Metropolitan Opera House when he conducted a brilliant new production of Verdi's *Falstaff*. In 1969 Leonard Bernstein became "laureate conductor" of the New York Philharmonic when he renounced his full-time duties in order to spend more time composing and writing. His most current work, *Mass,* for chorus and orchestra, will be played as part of the inaugural festivities of The John F. Kennedy Center for the Performing Arts.

Maria Callas
1923-

Although born at New York's Flower Hospital at Fifth Avenue and 106th Street, on 23 December 1923, Maria Callas began her professional career in Greece. Taken there in 1936 by her mother, one year later she was enrolled as a student at the National Conservatory in Athens. Her first stage appearance was in a student production of *Cavalleria rusticana* in 1938. Her debut in the title role of Puccini's *Tosca* with the Athens Opera in July of 1942 was the highlight of her early European career. She returned to New York for two years in 1945, but finding little impetus here for a career in opera she returned to Europe where she made her Italian debut in August of 1947 in the Arena at Verona. The opera was *La Gioconda;* the reviews were polite, but not overly enthusiastic. Then things began to happen: An Isolde and Turandot at La Fenice in Venice; another Isolde in Genoa; Elvira in Bellini's *I Puritani,* again at La Fenice. On 12 April 1950 she made her debut at the most sacred of all Italian shrines of opera, Milan's La Scala. The reviews of her Aïda that night praised her acting more than her singing. She became known as a singer who could sing anything, especially the fiendishly difficult roles of the bel canto repertory. Operas of the first half of the nineteenth century which had not been heard for decades were revived for her. She was compared with Maria Malibran, Giuditta Pasta, and with other voices who are legends in the annals of operatic performance. So popular had she become at La Scala that she was chosen to sing in the opening-night opera of all seasons but one from 1951 to 1955. On 1 November 1954 she returned in triumph to the United States, singing the title role of Bellini's *Norma* with the Lyric Opera of Chicago. The response by press and by public indicated that a new era in operatic history in America had begun. She made her Metropolitan Opera debut, again as the ill-fated Celtic priestess, Norma, on 29 October 1956. A month later New York saw the full force of her dramatic ability in performances of Puccini's *Tosca*. In 1958 Dallas audiences rose to cheer her interpretation of the vengeful heroine of Luigi Cherubini's *Medea,* an opera resurrected from the obscurity of time's dusty clouds by her presence on the operatic stage. As she achieved celebrity, the gossip columns of the papers constantly reported the fortunes and misfortunes of her private life, while the music critics praised her one-woman act of resurrecting a golden age of opera. She has not created any new roles to serve as examples for future singers, but she has re-created the leading soprano roles in the florid operas of the past century, and has brought life into lyric characters who too often appeared as lifeless animated cutouts. "La Divina," as her most fervent admirers call her, added a new aspect to her career when, in 1970, she began a series of teaching lectures at New York's Juilliard School of Music.

82. Maria Callas
by Henry Koerner, 1956
Oil on canvas, 28 x 22
Lent by *Time, the Weekly Newsmagazine*

MARIA CALLAS
by HENRI MAGNIN
TIME — OCTOBER 29, 1956

Leonard Warren was born in New York City on 21 April 1911 and after graduation from Columbia University decided to try for a career in music. He sang for a while with the Glee Club at Radio City Music Hall and in 1938 won the Metropolitan Opera Auditions, although he knew only about five operatic arias and had had no stage experience. After a short six months of study in Italy he first sang at the Metropolitan in a concert late in 1938 and made his stage debut there on 13 January 1939 as Paolo in Verdi's *Simon Boccanegra.* Although not noted for the quality of his acting in his early seasons, he had a real stage presence and an impressive voice, and he slowly became the lead baritone of the old House at Broadway and 39th Street. He sang an impressive Barnaba for the first time in a performance of *La Gioconda* in February of 1940 and on 20 February 1942 created the role of Ilo in Gian-Carlo Menotti's *The Island God.* In the same year he appeared for the first time in South America at Rio de Janeiro's Teatro Municipal and began making appearances in the opera houses in Mexico City and Buenos Aires. It was in the Argentine capital that he first sang Rigoletto, one of his finest characterizations. The Metropolitan heard him as the hunchback jester for the first time on 18 December 1943. On 16 May 1958 he sang the role at Moscow's Bolshoi Theatre as one of the first American singers to appear in Russia as part of the cultural exchange program. He specialized in the dramatic roles of the standard repertory, and on most nights when Verdi was sung the third voice in the traditional triumvirate of soprano, tenor, and baritone was that of Leonard Warren. On 4 February 1959 he sang the hero-villain Macbeth in the Metropolitan's first production of the century-old Verdi thriller, and on 1 March 1960 he sang the performance that many of his critics found to be his greatest vocal and dramatic achievement up to that time. It was the title role in Verdi's *Simon Boccanegra,* the opera in which he had made his Met debut twenty-one years before. Three days later, as he finished the aria "Urna fatale" in a performance of the same composer's *La Forza del Destino,* he collapsed and the curtain was lowered on the performance and on a great career. He died backstage minutes later.

83. Leonard Warren as the Count di Luna in Giuseppe Verdi's *Il Trovatore* by Elizabeth Montgomery, 1964
Oil on canvas, 30 x 25
Lent by Mrs. Leonard Warren

Zero Mostel
1915-

Zero Mostel, born in Brooklyn on 28 February 1915, made his first public appearances in the theater in Greenwich Village club reviews. Moving uptown, he made his Broadway debut in April of 1942 at the 44th Street Theatre. The Production was a review called *Keep' Em Laughing*. He was Hamilton Peachum in *Beggar's Holiday* at the Broadway Theatre late in 1946 and Glubb in *Flight into Egypt* at the Music Box early in 1952. In July of the same year he played in his own adaptation of Moliere's *The Imaginary Invalid* at Cambridge, Massachusetts' Brattle Theatre. On 5 June 1958 at the Rooftop Theatre he opened as Leopold Bloom in *Ulysses in Nighttown*. Brooks Atkinson's comment in the *New York Times* of the following day, "Zero Mostel is the perfect Leopold Bloom," can be taken as a compliment of the highest order to both Mostel and Bloom. For his performance Zero Mostel won an "Obie" awarded by *The Village Voice* for an off-Broadway performance. Another success followed with the opening of a production of Eugene Ionesco's *Rhinoceros* at the Longacre Theatre on 9 January 1961. Walter Kerr's review in the *Hearld Tribune* humorously echoed the acclaim that all the New York critics lavished on Mostel for his reading of the part of John and gave a vivid description of the great scene of his metamorphosis into the wild animal: " 'Rhinoceros' is an entertainment in which an extremely talented rhinoceros plays Zero Mostel. . . . The shoulders lift, the head juts forward, one foot begins to beat the earth with such native majesty that dust—real dust—begins to rise like the after-veil that seems to accompany a safari." For this characterization, Mostel was the recipient of a "Tony." A third award, another "Tony," was in the not-too-distant future when *A Funny Thing Happened on the Way to the Forum* opened at the Alvin Theatre 8 May 1962 with Zero Mostel as the freedom-seeking slave Pseudolus. In the autumn of 1964 Mr. Mostel created the role of Tevye at the opening of a musical, *Fiddler on the Roof,* which by this time has become a Broadway monument. Like his ancestor in American comedy, Joseph Jefferson, Zero Mostel is a painter and many of his offstage hours are spent in his studio in mid-Manhattan, where his work is as prolific as his wisecracks. When preparing a role, Zero Mostel has often painted himself as the character he is about to play. His self-portraits as Bloom, John, and Tevye are unique artistic documents of his stage career.

84. Zero Mostel as John in Eugene Ionesco's *Rhinoceros*
by Zero Mostel, 1960
Oil on canvas, 34 x 30
Lent by Kathryn Productions

After graduation from high school in Laurel, Mississippi, Leontyne Price studied at Central State College in Ohio and at the Juilliard School of Music in New York. Her stage debut in that city was made at the Broadway Theatre on 16 April 1952 as Saint Cecilia in a revival of Virgil Thompson's opera *Four Saints in Three Acts*. Later that same year she toured Europe with a triumphantly received revival of George Gershwin's *Porgy and Bess,* singing the role of Bess. Returning to the United States, the production opened at New York's Ziegfield Theatre on 10 March 1953 where Miss Price alternated her role with another soprano for the run of 305 performances. On 30 October 1953 she began a long and comfortable association with the music of Samuel Barber when she premiered his *Hermit Songs* in concert at the Library of Congress in Washington, D.C., with the composer as her accompanist. The following year she sang the premiere of Barber's *Prayers of Kierkegaard* with the Boston Symphony. In 1955 she was seen on television for the first time in the title role of Puccini's *Tosca* with the NBC Opera. Miss Price's debut with a major opera company came when she sang the role of the New Prioress in the American premiere of Francis Poulenc's *Dialogue of the Carmelites* at the San Francisco Opera 20 September 1957. Her debuts with opera houses in Vienna, London, Chicago, Salzburg, Berlin, and Milan followed in rapid succession. On 27 January 1961 Leontyne Price made her debut with the Metropolitan Opera as Leonora in Verdi's *Il Trovatore*. The appearance on America's most prestigious operatic stage of such an outstanding homegrown talent was recognized and hailed by all the critics. In 1964 Miss Price added further glory to her professional reputation when she appeared at Moscow's Bolshoi Theatre as a guest artist with the visiting La Scala Opera of Milan. To her also went what many consider the outstanding operatic honor of this century—the privilege of opening the new Metropolitan Opera House in New York's Lincoln Center in a role written especially for her. On 16 September 1966 the curtains of the new house parted on a grandiose production of her old friend Samuel Barber's *Antony and Cleopatra* with Justino Diaz and Leontyne Price in the title roles. It was a personal truimph of the greatest magnitude for Miss Price, but the opera, weighted down by an overpowering and cumbersome production, disappeared from the stage of the new opera house after a scant half-dozen performances in the first season. In recognition of her talent and achievements Miss Price has received many awards and honors: among them, the Order of Merit of Italy, the Presidential Medal of Freedom, and the Spingarn Medal of the NAACP.

85. Leontyne Price as Cleopatra in Samuel Barber's
Antony and Cleopatra
by Elizabeth Montgomery, 1967
Oil on canvas, 25 x 30
Lent by Leontyne Price

Joan Baez was born on Staten Island, New York, on 9 January 1941, grew up in towns from coast to coast, and bought her first guitar from a mail-order house when she was in high school in Palo Alto, California. After high school, her family moved to Boston and she began her professional career there, singing in the coffeehouses in the university areas on both sides of the Charles River. She hit the big time when she appeared at the 1959 Folk Festival at Newport, Rhode Island. Recording companies vied for her favors, and she finally signed a contract with the stipulation that she only be required to record one album a year. Soon after her recording debut, she became the first folk musician ever to have an album on the charts of best sellers. By November of 1962, three of her albums achieved the same degree of commercial prominence at the same time. On 23 November 1967, her portrait was featured on the cover of *Time,* which called her the "tangible sibyl" of folk music in America. Her repertory of the folk singers' standard bag of old English and Scottish songs was augmented with works by the young Bob Dylan and with increasing numbers of songs of protest, as her professional engagements became a sounding board for her personal views on the turbulent American scene in the late sixties. Musically, she achieved a style which was copied by many aspiring young folk singers. In acquiescence to a growing taste for electric rock, she is said to have made one album in that mood in 1967, but it was never released. In the same year she became actively involved in the activities of a school for nonviolence and her concert appearances became fewer in number. In late summer of 1967, Joan Baez was denied the use of Constitution Hall in Washington, D.C., because of her outspoken views against the war in Southeast Asia and her refusal to pay income tax. Thereupon she received permission from the Department of the Interior to give a free concert on the grounds of the Washington Monument. She performed on the evening of 14 August 1967 before a crowd variously estimated at from 10,000 to 30,000 people. Carl Bernstein, reporting in the *Washington Post* the following morning, called the concert a "monumental personal and musical triumph" for Joan Baez.

86. Joan Baez
by Russell Hoban, 1962
Casein on board, 32 x 25
Lent by *Time, The Weekly Newsmagazine*

Helen Hayes
1900-

Helen Hayes made her debut in 1905 on the stage of the National Theatre in her native Washington, D.C., where she was born on 10 October 1900. Her first role, a premonition of grander royalty to come later, was Prince Charles in a Columbia Players' production of *The Royal Family*. Her New York debut was also made as a child actress when she opened as Little Mimi in *Old Dutch* at the Herald Square Theatre on 22 November 1909. One of her first successes as an adult was as Margaret in *Dear Brutus* which opened at the Empire Theatre on 23 December 1918. On 13 April 1925 Calvin Coolidge pushed a button in the Nation's Capital and gave the signal to raise the curtain on the first production in the Theatre Guild's new playhouse. Appropriately enough, the heroine of that production of Shaw's *Caesar and Cleopatra* was Helen Hayes. She was again to star in the title role of a Theatre Guild production when Maxwell Anderson's *Mary of Scotland* opened in New York's Alvin Theatre on 27 November 1933. The crown passed to her again when she created one of her most unforgettable roles at the opening of *Victoria Regina* on 26 December 1935. Her portrayal of the young and the aged Queen Victoria won her both a Drama League of New York award and the satisfaction of a successful tour. Her Broadway debut in a Shakespearean role occurred in another Theatre Guild production. It was the season of 1940–1941 and the role was Viola in *Twelfth Night*. Somewhere along her busy and popularly received career she was aptly dubbed "The First Lady of the American Theatre." A Helen Hayes Festival at the Falmouth Playhouse during the summer of 1954, featuring Miss Hayes in re-creations of her original roles in *What Every Woman Knows, The Wisteria Tree,* and *Mary of Scotland,* was a testimony to her loyal following. In 1960 and 1961 she was recognized as a valuable cultural property by the United States Department of State which sent her on a tour of twenty-eight countries in Europe and South America. She was seen as Mrs. Antrobas in Thornton Wilder's *The Skin of Our Teeth* and as Amanda in Tennessee Williams' *The Glass Menagerie*. In the summer of 1962 she appeared with Maurice Evans in a program of readings from Shakespeare at the Stratford, Connecticut, American Shakespeare Festival and toured with the production during the season 1962–1963. Although her greater moments have been on the New York stage she has not forgotten her home town. A long-time friend of the Drama Department of the Catholic University of America in Washington, D.C., she has supported its endeavors by appearing in its productions. Her most recent appearance with the University's Hartke Theater was as Mary Tyrone in Eugene O'Neill's *Long Day's Journey into Night* in May 1971. She announced it as her farewell to the American stage.

87. Helen Hayes
by Furman J. Finck, 1966
Oil on canvas, 66 x 40

Lent by the artist through the courtesy of Capricorn Galleries, Bethesda, Maryland

Pablo Casals
1876-

Born 29 December 1876 in Vendrell, Spain, Pau Casals, or Pablo as he is generally known, received his early musical training from his father, a church organist. At age eleven he entered the school of music in Barcelona as a student of cello, and two years later played his first concert. After further study in Madrid and Brussels, he became cello soloist with the Paris Opéra in 1895, and in 1898 made his debut in Paris and London as a concert soloist. In 1901 he made his first trip to the United States for a tour of eighty concerts with soprano Emma Nevada and violinist Léon Moreau, under the management of Isadora Duncan's brother Raymond. While mountain climbing in California, a falling rock broke his left hand and his career as an instrumentalist was nearly ended. He recovered use of his hand, however, and made a second tour of the United States in 1904. During that tour he played as cello soloist in the first New York performance of Richard Strauss' *Don Quixote* under the composer's baton, and played at the White House for President Theodore Roosevelt. A short time later he was recognized as the world's foremost cello virtuoso. His playing of Bach suites in particular was especially noteworthy and was responsible for their reintroduction into the active concert repertory. During World War I he began to live part time in New York, and it was there, in 1916, that he, Paderewski, Kreisler, John McCormack, and other artists performed the memorable concert at the Metropolitan Opera House in honor of Spanish composer Enrique Granados, who was killed aboard a ship torpedoed in the English Channel. After the war, Casals concertized widely in both Europe and America. Loyal to the republican government of Spain, he played many concerts for war relief after the start of the Civil War. At the fall of Barcelona in the late thirties, he went into voluntary exile and settled at Prades in the south of France. It was there in 1957 that he began his famed Bach Festival. Because of illness in 1957, he was unable to conduct a festival he had arranged in San Juan, Puerto Rico. The festival was then held in his honor. Shortly afterward, Casals moved to San Juan, where he helped organize Puerto Rico's first truly native symphony orchestra and then served as president of the newly founded Puerto Rico Conservatory of Music. He was one of the artists invited to play in the General Assembly of the United Nations in New York in 1958 at a concert commemorating the thirteenth anniversary of the organization's founding. With Mieczyslaw Horszwski, he played Bach's *Sonata No. 2 in D Major* for cello and piano as part of a New York-Paris-Geneva concert transmitted by radio and television to seventy-four countries. On the evening of 13 November 1961 he played again in the White House at the invitation of President and Mrs. Kennedy. In 1963 he appeared at the UN a second time, conducting a performance of his own oratorio, *El Pessebre,* which he offered on tour as a personal peace crusade. On 4 May 1971, in honor of his services to music and humanity, the Organization of American States named Pau Casals an "honorary citizen of all the Americas." In June of 1971 he conducted, at age 94, the annual festival which he had founded in Puerto Rico.

88. Pablo Casals
by Furman J. Finck, 1966
Pencil on gesso sized board, 32½ x 23½
Lent by the Artist through the Courtesy of Portraits, Inc.

PAU
CASALS

Regina Resnik
1921-

Regina Resnik made her first appearances on stage in student productions of Gilbert and Sullivan operettas at New York's Hunter College. In 1942 she was engaged by the New York City opera where she made her debut as Lady Macbeth in the Verdi operatic version of Shakespeare's *Macbeth*. The following year she had entered the Metropolitan Opera Auditions of the Air and had progressed to the finals when she dropped out to sing several performances of Wagner in Mexico City. In 1944 she again entered the Auditions, was the only woman finalist, and received a contract from the Metropolitan Opera. She was scheduled to make her debut with that company as Santuzza in *Cavalleria rusticana,* but the indisposition of another soprano found her making her debut on 6 December 1944 as Leonora in Giuseppe Verdi's *Il Trovatore* on twenty-four hours' notice and without either orchestral or stage rehearsal. Until 1953 she sang the more or less standard soprano roles of the repertoire ranging from Rosalinde in *Die Fledermaus* to Sieglinde in *Die Walküre,* a role which she sang in 1953 at that year's Bayreuth Festival. After adding several mezzo-soprano parts to her repertory, the title role in *Carmen,* Venus in *Tannhäuser,* and the Princess Eboli in Verdi's *Don Carlo,* she decided about 1955 to forsake the soprano range and be a mezzo-soprano. It is in this lower voice range that she has achieved her most notable success. In the fall of 1957 she made her Convent Garden debut as Carmen. The appreciative reviews by the English critics were among the first she received over the years as one of the more popular interpreters of the popular role. The following year she returned to the same opera house to sing Marina in the Russian-language production of *Boris Godunov* that opened the 1958–1959 season. On 15 January 1958 she created the role of the Old Baroness in the Metropolitan Opera world premiere of Samuel Barber's *Vanessa*. In recent years she has become noted for her singing and acting of the tortured, guilt-ridden Klytämnestra in Richard Strauss's *Elektra*. After she sang it at the Metropolitan in the spring of 1971, a critic of the *New York Times* called it "a role she has made her own." Also in the spring of 1971 she began a career as a director of opera when she teamed with artist Arbit Blatas to design and direct a production of *Carmen* for the Hamburg Opera and one of *Elektra* for the Teatro La Fenice in Venice. After a performance in late June, the audience awarded *Carmen* an astounding fifty-three curtain calls. The Nation's Capital, which heard her strong performance of Madame Flora in Gian-Carlo Menotti's *The Medium* during the Washington Opera Society season of 1970–1971, will hear Miss Resnik's Klytämnestra for the first time in March of 1972 when she sings three concert performances of *Elektra* at the Kennedy Center with the National Symphony Orchestra.

89. Regina Resnik as Klytämnestra in Richard Strauss' *Elektra*
by Arbit Blatas, 1969
Oil on canvas, 75 x 39
Lent by the Artist

Marilyn Horne was seven years old when she began her formal voice training in Buffalo, New York, not far from her hometown of Bradford, Pennsylvania, where she was born in 1934. In 1945 her family moved to California, and it was there that she began her professional career as a singer with the Roger Wagner Chorale. After further voice study at the University of Southern California, she sang her first solo concerts in Los Angeles and made her operatic debut in 1954 in a Los Angeles Opera Guild production of Bedřich Smetana's *The Bartered Bride*. The following year she was the singing voice of Dorothy Dandridge on the soundtrack of the movie *Carmen Jones*. A European debut at the 1956 Venice Biennale was followed by an apprenticeship with the local opera company in Gelsenkirchen, Germany. Returning to the United States in 1960, she made her San Francisco Opera debut as Marie in Alban Berg's *Wozzeck* in the autumn of that year, and in February of 1961 Miss Horne made her New York operatic debut at Carnegie Hall in a concert performance of Bellini's *Beatrice di Tenda*. The performance was also the occasion of the New York debut of the Australian soprano Joan Sutherland, and although the *New York Times* was later to enthuse over joint appearances by the two ladies, it did not mention Marilyn Horne in its review of the *Beatrice*. Her Covent Garden debut, as Marie in *Wozzeck* again, was decidedly more successful, and when she returned to Carnegie Hall for another American Opera Society production in 1964— Rossini's *Semiramide*—audiences screamed and critics raved. In 1969 Milan's La Scala revived Rossini's *Assedio di Corinto* with a largely American cast. Marilyn Horne's bravura singing of a notoriously difficult fourteen-minute aria was understandably a high point of the performance. On Tuesday 3 March 1970 she made her debut at the Metropolitan Opera House in a new production of Bellini's *Norma*. Singing Adalgisa to the Norma of her friend Joan Sutherland, she was loudly applauded the moment she appeared on stage—even before she had sung a note. The press did anything but pass over her performance this time. The following Thursday, Harold Schonberg in the *New York Times* was moved to superlatives describing her solo passages and her duets with Miss Sutherland. *Time* on 16 March said, "Horne, making one of the greatest Met debuts, showed a vocal reach and a richness that exceeded nearly anybody's grasp." In the season of 1970–1971, the Lyric Opera of Chicago staged Rossini's *L'Italiana in Algeri* as a showcase for her particular talent, and she appeared as Rosina in the same composer's *Il Barbiere de Siviglia* at the Met. On 24 September 1971 she joins forces again with Joan Sutherland for an evening of blood-and-thunder bel canto when Chicago's Lyric Opera opens its season with a new production of Rossini's *Semiramide*.

90. Marilyn Horne as Adalgisa in Vincenzo Bellini's *Norma*
by John Foote, 1971
Oil on canvas, 50 x 36
Lent by the Artist

John Foote.

Barbra Streisand
1942-

A graduate of Brooklyn, New York's Erasmus High School in 1958, Barbra Streisand made her first appearance onstage in a revue entitled *Another Evening with Harry Stoones* at the Gramercy Arts Theatre on 21 October 1961. The following spring she opened at the Shubert Theatre, 22 March 1962 in Harold Rome's *I Can Get it for You Wholesale.* By the time she got through her big number "Miss Marmelstein" her role was anything but secondary. Audiences and critics sat up and noticed. When the show closed after 300 performances in December of 1962, Miss Streisand was on her way to stardom. For her performance as the zany secretary Miss Marmelstein, Barbra Streisand was cowinner of the *Variety* New York Drama Critics' Poll and received the *Cue* magazine award as entertainer of the year for 1963. She swiftly built up a loyal and vociferous following through club dates in New York and on the West Coast. On 5 October 1963 she appeared in concert with Sammy Davis, Jr., at the Hollywood Bowl. A measure of her popularity was the appearance of two record albums of her songs between May and October of that year. On 13 January 1964 she premiered at Boston's Shubert Theatre as Fanny Brice in Jule Styne's and Bob Merrill's *Funny Girl.* After a short run in Philadelphia, the show opened on 26 March at New York's Winter Garden with Barbra Streisand acknowleged as one of the first real old-fashioned, full-fledged stars that Broadway had experienced in years. Her performance in *Funny Girl* brought her more recognition in the form of a nomination for a Tony as best actress in a musical for 1964. Broadway has not seen her since the close of *Funny Girl,* most of her performing time being devoted to television work and Hollywood, where she starred in the film versions of the musicals *Funny Girl, Hello Dolly!,* and *On a Clear Day You Can See Forever.*

91. Barbra Streisand as Fanny Brice
in Jule Styne's and Bob Merrill's *Funny Girl*
by Philip Davison, 1968
Oil on canvas, 15½ x 11½
Lent by Barbra Streisand

Andrés Segovia
1894-

Andrés Segovia was born in Linares in the province of Catalonia in Spain, the son of an attorney. Against the wishes of family and friends he decided not to study violin, but the guitar, which, although a most important instrument in Spanish music, had not been seriously played in the concert hall. Even after he entered the Musical Institute in Granada he found little enthusiasm and encouragement from his instructors. He made his concert debut in Granada in 1909 and received only mild critical acclaim for his technique and musicianship. It was not until he made a tour of South America in 1919 that he was truly recognized for his unique contributions to concert music. While well grounded in the traditional idiom of Spanish guitar music, he had evolved a technique with an intensity of expression and a gradation of color and nuance that went beyond the traditional. In January of 1928 Andrés Segovia played his first concert in the United States at New Yorks' Town Hall. Included in the program were transcriptions for guitar of the music of Bach—for which he was later to become especially renowned—and Haydn. His listeners and the professional critics were lavish in their praise and there were those among them who placed Segovia in that select circle of virtuoso instrumentalists which included Fritz Kreisler and Pablo Casals. Critic Olin Downes, commenting upon the new guitar technique being introduced by Segovia, wrote in one of his reviews: "He draws the tone colors of a half a dozen instruments from the one he plays. He has an extraordinary command of nuances, he seems to discover whole planes of sonority. Although his instrument does not furnish a genuinely connected series of tone, he produces upon it very frequently the illusion of sustained song. . . ." Other critics were amazed by his ability to simulate the full choired effects of polyphony. So well received was Andrés Segovia after this debut concert that, within the next five weeks, he played over thirty additional concerts in the New York area. Since the time of his debut in the United States, Segovia has been recognized as the world's greatest guitarist. His concert dates in this country are eagerly awaited by his fans, and his numerous recordings, especially his transcriptions of the works of Bach, are considered the most definitive performances in his field of music.

92. Andrés Segovia
by Una Hanbury, 1968
Bronze, 16½ inches high
Lent by the Artist

Born in Seattle 27 November 1945, Jimi Hendrix started playing the electric guitar at age twelve. After serving with the United States Army, he played in almost fifty rock and roll groups from the West Coast to Greenwich Village before going to England in 1966. There, backed up by bass and drum, the Jimi Hendrix Experience conquered the popular music scene in about six months' time. Readers of the English pop-music papers voted him the world's "top musician." The Experience made its first appearance in the United States at the Monterey Pop Festival in June of 1967. The actions of Jimi Hendrix on stage were as violent as his music—one of his biographers called him a "psychedelic hootchie-kootchie man"—and even less subtly erotic. Later in the summer of 1967 the Experience started on its first American tour as a backup group to The Monkees. The hue and cry that went up after Hendrix's exhibition of guitar nuzzling and pelvic thrusts forced the Experience off the remainder of the Monkees' tour. The resultant publicity, his showmanship, and his musicianship all combined to put Jimi Hendrix right at the top with the leading rock groups—the Beatles and the Rolling Stones—and with Bob Dylan within a year's time. One of his more monumental musical performances was his playing of his own shattering version of "The Star-Spangled Banner" at the musical orgy held at Woodstock, New York, in August of 1969. Later that year the Experience broke up, but Jimi Hendrix reappeared at New York's Fillmore East on New Year's Eve with a new group, the Band of Gypsies, which in turn was dissolved only a few weeks later. In the spring of 1970 the Experience was re-formed. They had just finished a tour of Europe and had performed in the late summer Isle of Wight Festival when Jimi Hendrix died of an overdose of barbiturates in London on 18 September 1970.

93. Jimi Hendrix
by Jack Gregory, 1971
Polyester resin, 15 inches high
Lent by *Playboy*

94. Tragedy
by William Rush, 1808
Wood, 101½ high
Lent by Edwin Forrest Home

95. Comedy
by William Rush, 1808
Wood, 104 high
Lent by Edwin Forrest Home
The figures of Comedy and Tragedy were carved for the
facade of the Chestnut Street Theatre in Philadelphia and
somehow escaped destruction when it burned. They were
put in place when the new building was opened in 1820 and
remained there until 1855 when they were acquired by
Edwin Forrest.

96. Scene from *School for Scandal*
by William Dunlap
Oil on canvas, 25 x 30
Lent by Harvard Theatre Collection

97. Scene from *The Spy*
by William Dunlap, 1829
Oil on canvas, 21¾ x 26¾
Lent by New York State Historical Association
The actors in both paintings have been identified as
Joseph Jefferson I, John Hodgkinson, Eliza Whitlock, and
Joseph Tyler.

98. *Durang's Horn Pipe*
Published by E. Riley, date uncertain
Sheet music, large quarto, trimmed
Lent by Library of Congress, Music Division

99. Playbill, Chestnut Street Theatre, Philadelphia,
17 January 1835
William B. Wood in *Gustavus III*
Paper, 7½ x 18¼
Lent from a private collection

100. Playbill, no theater listed, 11 March 1811
George Frederick Cooke in *Richard III*
Paper, 8¾ x 6¾
Lent by Crawford Theatre Collection,
Yale University Library

101. Edmund Kean as Alanienouidet
by G. F. Storm after Frederick Meyer, Jr.
Published by Neal & Mackenzie, Philadelphia, 1828
Stipple and line engraving, 15⅜ x 10¾
Lent by Harvard Theatre Collection

102. Maria Garcia Malibran as Rosina in Rossini's
Il Barbiere di Siviglia
by A. E. Chalon, 1825
Pen and watercolor on paper, 11⅞ x 4⅞
Lent by Victoria and Albert Museum
This caricature was drawn in London just prior to the first
appearance of the Garcia troupe in New York. The famed
soprano is shown in the same role in which she made her
American debut.

103. "Una voce poco fa" from Rossini's
Il Barbiere di Siviglia
Published by Dubois and Stoddart, New York,
probably 1826
Sheet music, large quarto
Lent by Library of Congress, Music Division

104 a and b. Engrossed certificates presented to
Ira Aldridge by Russian actors in St. Petersburg in 1858
Paper, 21⅝ x 15½ and 17½ x 17¾
Lent by Victoria and Albert Museum

105. Sandals worn by Edwin Forrest in *The Gladiator*
Lent by The Players

106. Tomahawk carried by Edwin Forrest in *Metamora*
Lent by The Players

107. Playbill, Chestnut Street Theatre, 10 December 1830
Edwin Forrest in *Metamora*
Paper, 21½ x 6
Lent by Crawford Theatre Collection,
Yale University Library

108. Great Riot at the Astor Place Opera House,
New York, on Thursday Evening 10 May 1849
Published by Nathaniel Currier, 1849
Lithograph on paper, 8¹³⁄₁₆ x 12¾ , plus margins
Lent by Library of Congress, Division of Prints and
Photographs

109. Playbill for Walnut Street Theatre, Philadelphia,
15 March 1833
Fanny Kemble in *Fazio*
Paper, 17 x 5½
Lent by Free Library of Philadelphia, Theatre Collection

110. Letter from Mary Ann Wood to Charlotte Cushman,
dated 23 January 1835
Lent by Library of Congress, Manuscript Division

111. "As I View These Scenes So Charming" from
Bellini's *La Sonnambula*
Published by Fiot, Meignen & Co., Philadelphia,
probably 1836
Sheet music, large quarto, trimmed
Lent by Free Library of Philadelphia,
Sheet Music Collection

112. "False One—I Love Thee Still" from
Vincenzo Bellini's *La Sonnambula*
Published by Atwill's Music Saloon, New York,
probably 1836
Sheet music, large quarto, trimmed
Lent by Free Library of Philadelphia,
Sheet Music Collection
It bears an idealized likeness that may be intended as a
portrait of Mary Ann Wood as Amina.

113. Miniature of Fanny Kemble on a bracelet of her hair.
Lent by Folger Shakespeare Library
Owned by Charlotte Cushman, the miniature was a gift from Rosalie Sully who probably was also the artist. Inscribed on reverse: Charlotte from Rosalie, July 22nd 1844.

114. English china saucer from a tea set presented to Charlotte Cushman in England, 1846
Lent by Folger Shakespeare Library

115. Playbill for Tremont Theatre, Boston, 8 April 1835
Charlotte Cushman and Clara Fisher in Mozart's
Marriage of Figaro
Paper, 15 x 6⅞
Lent from a private collection

116. Playbill, Washington Theatre, Washington, D.C.,
6 February 1861
Charlotte Cushman as Hamlet
White silk, 16 x 5½
Lent by Library of Congress, Manuscript Division

117. Charlotte Cushman
by F. Gutekunst, 1874
Cabinet photo, 6½ x 4⅜
Lent from a private collection

118. Autograph letter from Mary Ann Lee to her southern managers, Ludlow and Lee, dated at Philadelphia
21 September 1846. She suggested a production of
Giselle.
Lent by Harvard Theatre Collection

119. Playbill for Park Theatre, New York, 14 April 1846
Mary Ann Lee in *Giselle*
Paper, 21 9/16 x 5¼
Lent by Harvard Theatre Collection

120. Castanets used by Fanny Elssler
Lent by Dance Collection, The New York Public Library,
Gift of Friends of the Dance Collection

121. Girandole with base depicting Fanny Elssler dancing the Cachucha
Possibly of American manufacture, circa 1841
Gold-washed bronze, marble and crystal, 21¾ high
Lent by Dance Collection, The New York Public Library.
Gift of Friends of the Dance Collection

122. Flask depicting Fanny Elssler dancing the Cachucha
Unidentified glassworks, circa 1841
Glass, 7¾ high
Lent by Dance Collection, The New York Public Library,
Gift of Friends of the Dance Collection

123. Fanny Elssler dancing the Cachucha
Published by Nathaniel Currier, New York, circa 1840
Lithograph, 12 x 9, plus margins, hand colored
Lent from a private collection

124. *La Cracovienne as danced by Fanny Elssler*
Published by Hewitt & Jones, New York, probably 1840
Sheet music cover, large quarto, trimmed
Lent by Library of Congress, Division of Prints and Photographs

125. *La Gitana (The New Cachoucha) danced by Madlle Fanny Elssler*
Published by Firth & Hall, New York, probably 1840
Sheet music, large quarto, trimmed
Lent by Library of Congress, Division of Prints and Photographs

126. Playbill for the Park Theatre, New York, 27 May 1840
Fanny Elssler in *L'Amour*
Paper, 5¾ x 23
Lent from a private collection

127. George Washington Smith in dance costume
by T. R. Burnham, Boston, circa 1860
Carte-de-visite photo, 4 x 2½
Lent by Dance Collection, The New York Public Library
As the only American premier danseur noble of the nineteenth century, Smith partnered Fanny Elssler and many of the great female dancers who appeared here.

128. Tobacco label depicting Jenny Lind
Copyrighted by Boggs & Gregory, New York, 1850
Paper, 4¾ x 4⅜
Lent by Library of Congress, Division of Prints and Photographs

129. *Jenny Lind's Greeting to America*
Lithograph by A. Schwartz and F. Moné, printed by
Nagel & Weingaertner, New York, copyright by
Samuel C. Jollie, 1850
Lithograph, 21¼ x 17½, plus margins
Lent by Library of Congress, Division of Prints and Photographs

130. *A Collection of the Most Admired Songs of Jenny Lind*
Published by Oliver Ditson, Boston, probably 1850
Sheet music, large quarto, trimmed
Lent by Library of Congress, Division of Prints and Photographs
The cover lithograph by B. W. Thayer & Co., after a daguerreotype by Whipple, depicts Jenny Lind, the tenor Giovanni Belletti, and the conductor Julius Benedict.

131. *The Banjo* by Louis Moreau Gottschalk
Published by Wm. Hall & Son, 1855
Sheet music, large quarto, trimmed
Lent by Library of Congress, Music Division

132. *Murmurs Aeolian* by Louis Moreau Gottschalk
Published by Wm. Hall and Co., 1862
Sheet music, large quarto, trimmed
Lent by Library of Congress, Music Division

133. *The Last Hope* by Louis Moreau Gottschalk
Published by Firth, Pond & Co., 1854
Sheet music, large quarto, trimmed
Lent by Library of Congress, Music Division

134. Shoulder drapery worn by Edwin Booth in *Hamlet*
Lent by Museum of the City of New York,
Theatre and Dance Collection

135. Crown worn by Edwin Booth in *Richard III*
Lent by The Players

136. *"Ha! I like not that!"*
by John Rogers, 1882
Bronze, 22 high
Lent by The New-York Historical Society
The figure of Iago is a portrait of Edwin Booth. That of
Othello is thought to represent Tomasso Salvini.

137. Playbill for Arch Street Theatre, Philadelphia,
29 August 1859
Edwin Booth and John McCullough in *Othello*
Paper, 19½ x 8¼
Lent by Crawford Theatre Collection,
Yale University Library

138. John Wilkes, Edwin, and Junius Brutus Booth, Jr., as
Marc Antony, Brutus, and Cassius in Shakespeare's
Julius Caesar, performed at the Winter Garden Theatre,
New York, 25 November 1864.
Cabinet photo, 8 x 6
Lent by McLellan Lincoln Collection, Brown University

139. Playbill for Brooklyn Academy of Music, 4 April 1891
Edwin Booth as Hamlet. His farewell performance.
Silk, 10 x 5¾
Lent by The Players

140. *Rip Van Winkle at Home*
by John Rogers,
Bronze, 18½ high
Lent by The New-York Historical Society

141. *Rip Van Winkle on the Mountain*
by John Rogers,
Bronze, 21¼ high
Lent by The New-York Historical Society

142. *Rip Van Winkle Returned*
by John Rogers,
Bronze, 21½ high
Lent by The New-York Historical Society
Numbers 140, 141, and 142 depict Joseph Jefferson in his
most famous role. They are bronze master models for the
popular plaster parlor ornaments which sold
originally for $12.00 each.

143. Dion Boucicault
by Spy (Sir Leslie Ward), published in
Vanity Fair, 16 December 1882
Lithograph, 12¼ x 7¼, plus margins
Lent from a private collection.

144. Adelina Patti
by B. J. Falk, 1887
Cabinet photo, 13 x 7½
Lent by Library of Congress, Division of Prints and
Photographs

145. Poster for Sarah Bernhardt American Tour
Strobridge Lithograph Co., New York
Lithograph, 76 x 24¼
Lent by Library of Congress, Division of Prints and
Photographs

146 a, b, and c. Sarah Bernhardt
by N. Sarony, 1880
Set of three cabinet photos, each 13 x 7½
Lent by Library of Congress, Division of Prints and
Photographs

147. Program, Boston Theatre, 28 February 1884
Henry Irving in *Much Ado About Nothing*
Paper, 12 x 8¾
Lent by Crawford Theatre Collection,
Yale University Library

148. Baton used by Anton Seidl
Lent by Metropolitan Opera Association

149. Anton Seidl's own transcriptions of music by
Richard Wagner, possibly copied out when he was
Wagner's assistant at Bayreuth
Holograph, large quarto
Lent by Metropolitan Opera Association

150. Playbill for the Garrick Theatre, Philadelphia,
March 1907
Richard Mansfield in *Beau Brummel*
Paper, 5½ x 17⅞
Lent from a private collection

151. Poster for *Mary of Magdala*
with Minnie Maddern Fiske, 1903
Published by Grignard Lithograph Co., New York
Lithograph, 27 x 16½
Lent by Library of Congress, Division of Prints and
Photographs

152. Lamp in the shape of Loie Fuller
Designed by Raoul Larche, circa 1900
Height 18
Lent by Lillian Nassau Collection

153. *La Loie Fuller*
Copyright by R. E. Stevens, 189(7)
Lithograph, 83 x 37
Lent by Library of Congress, Division of Prints and
Photographs

154. Program from the Théâtre de la Loïe Fuller at the
Paris Exposition, 1900
Paper, 5⅝ x 3¾
Lent by Dance Collection, The New York Public Library

155. Program for Loie Fuller performance at the Panama-Pacific International Exposition, San Francisco, 1 June 1915
Paper, 10$\frac{5}{16}$ x 6$\frac{15}{16}$
Lent by Dance Collection, The New York Public Library; Gift of Violet Romer

156. Loie Fuller
by B. J. Falk, 1901
Photo, 9$\frac{13}{16}$ x 7¼, mounted
Lent by Library of Congress, Division of Prints and Photographs

157. Shoulder scarf worn by Maude Adams in *The Little Minister*
Lent by Museum of the City of New York, Theatre and Dance Collection

158. Poster for James Barrie's *The Little Minister* with Maude Adams
Published by Strobridge Lithograph Co., New York, 1897
Lithograph, 31 x 23
Lent by Library of Congress, Division of Prints and Photographs

159. Costume worn by Julia Marlowe in *Twelfth Night*
Lent by Portsmouth Little Theatre, Portsmouth, Ohio

160. Julia Marlowe as Pauline in Edward Bulwer-Lytton's *The Lady of Lyons*
by B. J. Falk, 1888
Cabinet photo, 13 x 7½ mounted
Lent by Library of Congress, Division of Prints and Photographs

161. Julia Marlowe as Viola in Shakespeare's *Twelfth Night*
by B. J. Falk, 1890
Cabinet photo, 13 x 7½ mounted
Lent by Library of Congress, Division of Prints and Photographs

162. Costume worn by Enrico Caruso in *La Juive*
Lent by Metropolitan Opera Association

163. Voucher to Enrico Caruso's paycheck for a performance of *Pagliacci* at the Metropolitan Opera, 17 February 1915. As was his custom he appraised his own performance. On this check he has written, "Benissima," "Grande Ovazione," and "Ultimo."
Lent by Francis Robinson

164. *Lasciati amar* by Ruggiero Leoncavallo
Holograph, 8 pages, 14⅜ x 10
Lent by Peabody Institute Library, Baltimore; Maryland; Gift of Mrs. Dorothy Caruso
Inscribed by Enrico Caruso

165. Enrico Caruso as the Duke in Verdi's *Rigoletto*
by Aime Dupont, 1908
Cabinet photo, 6½ x 4¼
Lent by Library of Congress, Division of Prints and Photographs

166. Enrico Caruso as Dick Johnson in Puccini's *La Fanciulla del West*
by Mishkin, 1911
Photo, 8 x 5¾, mounted
Lent by Library of Congress, Division of Prints and Photographs

167. Knife carried by Geraldine Farrar in *Madame Butterfly*. Made for her in Japan and presented to her by noted traveler Burton Holmes, 1907.
Lent by Library of Congress, Music Division

168. Fan carried by Geraldine Farrar in *Manon*
Lent by Library of Congress, Music Division

169. Playbill, Metropolitan Opera, New York, opening week of 1920–1921 season
Paper, 28 x 5
Lent by Library of Congress, Music Division

170. Playbill, Metropolitan Opera, New York, ninth week of 1921–1922 season
Paper, 28 x 5
Lent by Library of Congress, Music Division

171. Baton used by Arturo Toscanini
Lent by Metropolitan Opera Guild

172. Baton used by John Philip Sousa when conducting the United States Marine Band
Lent by United States Marine Corps Museum

173. Group of medals awarded to John Philip Sousa
a. Royal Victorian Medal
b. Palmes Universitaires
c. "March King" Medal
d. Gold Medal of the American Academy of Arts and Sciences
Lent by United States Marine Corps Museum

174. *Semper Fidelis* by John Philip Sousa
Incomplete holograph, large quarto
Lent by United States Marine Corps Museum
Inscribed, also in the composer's hand: "To the Officers and Men of the United States Marine Corps."

175. Ballet slippers worn by Anna Pavlova
Lent by Dance Collection, The New York Public Library; Gift of Gertrude C. Adams

176. Program for an Anna Pavlova performance at the Metropolitan Opera House, 3 November 1914
Paper, 10$\frac{3}{16}$ x 7¼
Lent by Dance Collection, The New York Public Library

177. Program for Anna Pavlova's 1914–1915 American tour
Paper, 13¼ x 8½
Lent by Mrs. Otis Chatfield-Taylor

178. Anna Pavlova
by Arnold Genthe
Photo, 12¼ x 9⅞, mounted
Lent by Library of Congress, Division of Prints and Photographs

179. Design for costume worn by Vaslav Nijinsky in the
ballet *Le Spectre de la Rose*
by Leon Bakst, 1911
Mixed media on paper, 15½ x 10³⁄₁₆
Lent by Wadsworth Atheneum, The Ella Gallup Sumner
and Mary Catlin Sumner Collection

180. Costume worn by Ruth St. Denis in *Kwannon*
Lent by Dance Department,
University of California at Los Angeles

181. Program for the
Fourth Transcontinental Denishawn Tour, 1915
Paper, 9⅝ x 6½
Lent by Denishawn Collection, Dance Collection,
The New York Public Library

182. Costume worn by Ted Shawn in *Xochitl*
Lent by Ted Shawn

183. Fragment of costume worn by Isadora Duncan when
dancing *Primavera*
Lent by Irma Duncan Collection, Dance Collection,
The New York Public Library

184. Wreath of artificial flowers worn by Isadora Duncan
on her Russian tours when real flowers were not available
Lent by Irma Duncan Collection, Dance Collection,
The New York Public Library

185. Album of silkscreen facsimiles of Jules Grand'jouan
pastel drawings of Isadora Duncan. This album was the
personal property of the dancer.
Leatherbound volume, 19½ x 14½
Lent by Irma Duncan Collection, Dance Collection,
The New York Public Library

186. Program for Isadora Duncan European tour, 1907
Paper, 12¾ x 9¾
Lent by Augustin Duncan Collection, Dance Collection,
The New York Public Library

187. Program for Isadora Duncan performance at the
Metropolitan Opera House, 1908
Paper, 12 x 8¾
Lent by Irma Duncan Collection, Dance Collection,
The New York Public Library

188. Isadora Duncan dancing on the Acropolis
by Edward Steichen
Photo, 14 x 11, mounted
Lent by Library of Congress, Division of Prints and
Photographs

189. Isadora Duncan and her dance group
by Arnold Genthe, 1918 (?)
Photo, 10¼ x 10¼, irregular and mounted
Lent by Library of Congress, Division of Prints and
Photographs

190. Rendering for set of Act 1, Scene 1 of
Mourning Becomes Electra
by Robert Edmund Jones, 1931
Ink and watercolor on illustration board, 11½ x 15
Lent by Eugene and Carlotta O'Neill Collection,
Collection of American Literature, Beinecke Rare Book
and Manuscript Library, Yale University

191. Program for *The Chosen People* with Alla Nazimova
Paper, 8¾ x 6
Lent by Jean Kling Lewton

192. Poster for Otis Skinner Tour
Published by Courier Lithograph Co., Buffalo, New York,
1899
Lithograph, 78¾ x 39
Lent by Library of Congress, Division of Prints and
Photographs

193. Costume worn by Feodor Chaliapin in
Boris Godunov
Lent by Boris Chaliapin

194. Rendering of set for *Present Laughter*
by Donald Oenslager, 1936
Watercolor on paper, 10 x 25
Lent by the artist

195. Rendering for set of *Forsaking All Others*
by Donald Oenslager, 1933
Watercolor on paper, 5½ x 12
Lent by the artist

196. Tallulah Bankhead
by Al Hirschfeld
Ink on illustration board, 22 x 24½
Lent by the artist

197. Program for a Martha Graham performance at the
Guild Theatre, 27 February 1927
Paper, 9 x 6
Lent by Dance Collection, The New York Public Library

198. Costume worn by Angna Enters in *Queen of Heaven*
Lent by Angna Enters

199. *Caprice viennoise* by Fritz Kreisler
Incomplete holograph, large quarto
Lent by Library of Congress, Music Division

200. *O salutaris Hostia* by Fritz Kreisler
Holograph, three pages, large quarto
Lent by Library of Congress, Music Division
Inscribed, also in the composer's hand:
"To my dear friend John MacCormack [sic]."

201. John McCormack as Don Ottavio in Mozart's
Don Giovanni
by E. F. Foley, 1909
Photo, 7¹¹⁄₁₆ x 5⅞
Lent by Library of Congress, Division of Prints and
Photographs

202. Costume worn by Maurice Evans in *Richard II*
Lent by Museum of the City of New York,
Theatre and Dance Collection

203. Costume worn by Lucia Chase in *Capriccioso*
Lent by American Ballet Theatre

204. Rendering for set of *Capriccioso*
by Nicolas de Molas
Watercolor on paper, 22 x 32
Lent by American Ballet Theatre

205. Window card for Theatre Guild production of
Othello with Paul Robeson, 1943
Lithograph on cardboard, 22 x 14
Lent by Theatre Guild Archive,
Collection of American Literature, Beinecke Rare Book and
Manuscript Library, Yale University

206. Costume worn by Paul Robeson in *Othello*
Lent by Eaves Costume Company

207. Rendering for set of *Anything Goes*
by Donald Oenslager, 1934
Crayon and watercolor on paper, 15 x 24
Lent by the artist

208. Window card for Theatre Guild production of
Pygmalion with Lynn Fontanne, 1926
Lithograph on cardboard, 21⅝ x 13⅜
Lent by Theatre Guild Archive, Beinecke Rare Book and
Manuscript Library, Yale University

209. Overture to *Candide* by Leonard Bernstein
Holograph on transparent paper, 17⅛ x 9
Lent by Library of Congress, Music Division

210. Rendering for set of Act I of Verdi's *La Traviata*
by Franco Zeffirelli, 1958
Pastel on paper, 13½ x 18½
Lent by Lawrence V. Kelly, Dallas Civic Opera

211. Rendering for set of Act II, Scene 1 of *La Traviata*
by Franco Zeffirelli, 1958
Pastel on paper, 13½ x 18½
Lent by Lawrence V. Kelly, Dallas Civic Opera

212. Rendering for set of Act II, Scene 2 of *La Traviata*
by Franco Zeffirelli, 1958
Pastel on paper, 13½ x 18½
Lent by Lawrence V. Kelly, Dallas Civic Opera

213. Program, Dallas Civic Opera,
19 and 21 November 1959
Maria Callas in *Medea*
Paper, 9 x 6
Lent by Dallas Civic Opera

214. Rendering for costume worn by Leonard Warren
in *Rigoletto*
by Eugene Berman, 1951
Ink and watercolor on illustration board 12½ x 9½
Lent by Mrs. Leonard Warren

215. Rendering for costume worn by Leonard Warren
in *La Forza del Destino*
by Eugene Berman, 1952
Ink and watercolor on illustration board, 14 x 10¾
Lent by Mrs. Leonard Warren

216. Russian language score of Giuseppe Verdi's *Rigoletto*
presented to Leonard Warren after his performance at
Moscow's Bolshoi Opera on 16 May 1958. It is autographed
by all the other members of the cast of that performance.
Lent by Mrs. Leonard Warren

217. Costume worn by Zero Mostel in
A Funny Thing Happened on the Way to the Forum
Lent by Museum of the City of New York,
Theatre and Dance Collection

218. Caricature, Zero Mostel and Eli Wallach in *Rhinoceros*
by Al Hirschfeld, 1960
Ink on illustration board, 12 x 20
Lent by Anne Jackson-Eli Wallach Collection

219. Costume worn by Leontyne Price in
Antony and Cleopatra
Lent by Metropolitan Opera Association

220. Hat and cape worn by Helen Hayes in *Victoria Regina*
Lent by Museum of the City of New York,
Theatre and Dance Collection

221. Helen Hayes caricature
by Al Hirschfeld
Ink on illustration board, 25 x 21 framed
Lent by the artist

222. Window card for Theatre Guild production of
Caesar and Cleopatra with Helen Hayes, 1925
Lithograph on cardboard, 21⅝ x 13⅜
Lent by Theatre Guild Archive,
Collection of American Literature, Beinecke Rare Book and
Manuscript Library, Yale University

223. Window card for Theatre Guild production of
Mary of Scotland with Helen Hayes, 1933
Lithograph on cardboard, 21½ x 13⅜
Lent by Theatre Guild Archive,
Collection of American Literature, Beinecke Rare Book and
Manuscript Library, Yale University

224. Costume worn by Regina Resnik in *Elektra*
Lent by San Francisco Opera and Goldstein & Co.,
San Francisco

225. Program, Metropolitan Opera House, 3 March 1970
debut of Marilyn Horne in *Norma*
Paper, 11 x 8
Lent from a private collection

226. Vocal score of Vincenzo Bellini's *Norma*
autographed by Marilyn Horne at Adalgisa's entrance music
Paperbound volume, 10⅜ x 7
Lent from a private collection

Additional pictorial materials lent by Chicago Lyric Opera,
San Francisco Opera, United States Marine Corps Museum,
and Division of Photography, National Museum of History
and Technology, Smithsonian Institution.

Index

362

61   4   302